COASTAL CHANGES

COASTAL CHANGES

by

W. W. WILLIAMS

LONDON

ROUTLEDGE & KEGAN PAUL

*First published in 1960
by Routledge and Kegan Paul Ltd
Broadway House, 68–74 Carter Lane
London E.C.4*

*Printed in Great Britain
by Butler and Tanner Ltd
Frome and London*

© W. W. Williams 1960

CONTENTS

INTRODUCTION   xi

I.   THE GENERAL PROBLEM   I

II.   THE GEOLOGICAL BACKGROUND   9

III. PROCESSES OF EROSION, TRANSPORT
      AND DEPOSITION   40

IV.   THE IMPORTANCE OF WIND   88

V.   SOME COASTAL FORMS AND CHANGES   104

VI.   EVIDENCE OF CHANGES AND OBSER-
      VATIONAL METHODS   153

VII. SEA DEFENCES   185

      APPENDIX A   200

      APPENDIX B   204

      APPENDIX C   207

      APPENDIX D   208

      BIBLIOGRAPHY   213

      INDEX   217

FIGURES

	Map of England and Wales	*page* xx
II.1.	The effect of dipping strata on cliff formation	11
II.2.	Vertical sorting with shingle as a top layer	16
II.3.	Movement of beach material at Porthkerry	23
II.4.	Diagrammatic sketch of a tide gauge	33
II.5.	Variation of height of water in Mediterranean (at Algiers) and height of barometer	35
II.6.	Tide level trends at Aberdeen, Dunbar and Newlyn	36
III.1.	Trochoidal Waves	44
III.2.	Method of assessing wave heights at sea	46
III.3.	The formation of short crested waves	52
III.4.	Orbital motion of waves in deep water	55
III.5.	Orbital motion of waves on a beach	57
III.6.	'Mass transport' under wave action in a finite channel	58
III.7.	The constructive and destructive action of waves	60
III.8.	'Summer' and 'Winter' beach profiles	64
III.9.	The effect of wave action on a shingle beach	65
III.10.	Refraction of waves	66
III.11.	Distribution of wave energy on an indented coastline	68
III.12.	Tidal ranges at stations in the Bristol Channel	73
III.13.	Spring tide curves; continuous line Brest; broken line Le Havre	75
III.14.	The most effective winds for raising sea level at places on British coasts	83
III.15.	Actual and predicted tide curves for Southend— 31 January and 1 February 1953	85
III.16.	Rate of recession of cliffs at Covehithe, Suffolk	87
IV.1.	Sand Collectors; A. Saltation trap; B. Trap for surface creep	98
V.1.	The 'swash' bar	109
V.2.	Bar height to water depth ratio of offshore bar	110

vii

FIGURES

V.3.	Offshore bars; double series	*page* 113
V.4.	Formation of crescentic sandbars	114
V.5.	Profiles of a runnel and bar beach formation	117
V.6.	Growth of a spit	122
V.7.	Spits in S.E. Baltic	126
V.8.	Tombolas at Monte Argentario, Italy	130
V.9.	Spit, or tombolo at Nahant, Mass., U.S.A.	131
V.10.	Possible method of formation of tombolos	132
V.11.	Benacre, or Covehithe Ness, showing its movement since 1575	139
V.12.	Recurved Spits at Scolt Island, Norfolk	141
VI.1.	Contours of a beach, transferred from air photographs	161
VI.2.	Method of fixing soundings by plane table	166
VI.3.	Reducing soundings to datum	167
VI.4.	Fixing soundings by angles taken by one observer	169
VI.5.	Principles of echo-sounder	171
VI.6.	Admiralty type logships	176
VII.1.	The process of erosion, showing that the whole sea bed is lowered from AA′ to BB′ and then to CC′ etc.	185
VII.2.	Simplified section of seaward half of main dyke in reclamation of Zuider Zee	188
VII.3.	Simple groynes	190
VII.4.	Oblique groynes	193
VII.5.	Box groynes	193
VII.6.	Some sections of sea walls	195
	Appendices A—D	199

PLATES

I. *Upper.* Elegug Stacks, Pembrokeshire, in Carboniferous Limestone   *facing page*   44
   Lower. Sea stack and natural arch in schists. West Burra, Shetland   44

II. *Upper.* Short-crested waves in deep water   45
   Lower. Short-crested waves reflected—in a concentric series—by a wrecked ship   45

III. *Upper.* Erosion at the back of a sand beach during storm   60
   Lower. Runnel and bar formation. Near Morib, West Coast of Malaya   60

IV. *Upper.* Parallel offshore bars. West Coast of Italy   61
   Lower. Crescentic bars, double series. Anse de Pampelonne, Mediterranean France   61

V. Long-crested waves advancing upon, and being retarded by, the shelving beach in Saint Aubyn's Bay, Jersey   124

VI. *Upper.* Underwater feature between island and mainland   125
   Lower. Successive depositions on an Albanian beach, showing former shorelines now well inland   125

VII. Dunwich Church in 1904 and 1914. The church finally disappeared from the cliff top with a fall in 1919   140

VIII. A sea wall damaged by wave action   141

ix

INTRODUCTION

THE last few years have seen many additions to the literature on coastlines and coastal phenomena, and the subject has been dealt with so exhaustively that at first sight there may seem to be small justification for adding to the impressive array of publications now available to those who are interested in such matters. It is for this reason that the writing of this book has been delayed for ten years. Its ultimate appearance is due to two considerations: the first that most of the books available have been written from a standpoint which, while it deals fully with particular aspects of the problem, quite naturally and reasonably neglects others. The interests of the engineer, oceanographer, biologist and geographer differ very widely, and it is to be expected that the specialized interests of the one may ignore what is important to the other. The second consideration is that we appear to have reached an important stage in coastal investigations. Hitherto theories of coastal behaviour have been based on the most simple visual observations, and there is no doubt that some of these observations have been misleading. It would be wrong to belittle the work done by our forebears; their work has been honest and devoted, and their contributions are invaluable, but today new techniques are being developed which should lead to a more certain knowledge of the subject. This book is not a treatise on the new methods; rather it is a very brief statement of the stage which we have reached, and an opinion of the direction that future investigations should take.

My own interest in coastal phenomena began, as it is likely to end, in the idle contemplation of breakers hurling themselves against rocks, or rolling up sandy beaches. It was mental pictures of such scenes which prompted me to suggest, during the war of 1939–45, that beach gradients, all-important in amphibious military operations, might be determined from aerial photographs by measuring wave velocities and lengths, and then using well-known formulae for the computation of water depths. I was fortunate enough to be given the opportunity of developing the idea and it met with some success; but it then appeared that the beach profiles, and especially off-lying bars in the Mediterranean, were often changing at an alarming rate, and any assessment of the gradients of beaches or clearance over bars was likely to be out of date before it was published. Such intelligence is of course quite useless unless the intervening changes can be forecast in terms of the prevailing conditions of wind and sea. It was at this stage that I began to read the usual literature more critically, only to find that none of the authorities accessible to me had ventured to predict in any but the most general terms how the profile of a beach might be modified in differing conditions, and when they did predict, the reasons given were not always convincing. The problem is a very difficult one, and it cannot be claimed now that any sensational advances have been made. But advances *have* been made, and it can be fairly claimed that a few of the problems are solved. We benefit today from a host of new and ingenious instruments which are capable of yielding observations of the greatest value, and from the efforts of research workers well qualified to use them. But, unfortunately, there are great difficulties in using them where they are needed most, in the surf zones of large breaking wave systems.

This book is by design short, and is no more than a

brief introduction to a very large subject. I shall be very surprised if it is not criticized as being an over-simplification of the problems with which it attempts to deal. There would be some truth in this criticism; obviously the limitation of size means that much has been left out; but there is still much that is not understood, especially in problems of wave behaviour in surf, and in the resulting turbulence, and I have not deemed it useful to dwell at length upon what I do not understand. Also it can be said that what some may consider simplification is in fact clarification. Certainly I have been conscious as I have read through the very considerable literature on coastlines that it is over-encumbered with repeated irrelevancies or suppositions which in my opinion have confused the issue for too long. For this reason I have deliberately omitted much which other treatises accept as axiomatic but which I regard as unhelpful—if harmless—speculation. For example, I cannot accept Johnson's theory of the development of barrier islands from off-shore bars. Such a notion is open to very real objections as I have explained in the proper place in the following pages. But it has to be admitted that to find a satisfactory explanation of them is very difficult, and the matter is still, as far as I am aware, in the realm of supposition.

My difficulties with the usual textbooks may be explained by my particular point of view, for my interests prompt me to ask quite simply, 'What is happening?' or 'What is likely to happen next?' In such practical fields as war or engineering, when the price of mistakes can be so great, and the consequences of indecision so obvious, it is highly desirable that solutions of problems be not based on guesses, even if the guesses are intelligent; nor is it the case that a statement becomes more valid for being often repeated. The very essence of right thinking about coastal problems is to ascertain what agency is moving which material in which direction at what rate—and why.

Some of my readers may be surprised that I have not attempted to adopt or devise a systematic terminology for coastal features. I am aware that many writers have drawn up glossaries; I have not followed them, for on the one hand there are already too many in circulation, and on the other I have little reason to hope that if I suggested a new one it would be any better than its predecessors; neither am I concerned at nice distinctions between 'shore' and 'coast'; surely it can be left to the context to clarify the meaning of terms which, according to most dictionaries, are synonymous. Whether some of the more unusual names in use should be retained is another matter. The name 'Tombolo' can be reasonably applied to a feature which occurs in Italy: there is perhaps less justification for using the German 'Haff' for a feature which now exists in Poland or Russia. What is important is to be quite clear what we are talking or writing about.

It was after some hesitation that I decided to include a short chapter on coast defences, but I have done so because to discuss the disease without any reference to a cure seemed to paint too gloomy a picture. It will be clear to the experts in this field, the engineers, for whom I have the greatest respect and admiration, that this chapter is not intended for them, though I hope that the book as a whole may occasionally protect them from the ignorance and misguided optimism of some of those who employ them. The engineers must often have in mind what I think of as the *generation* factor, or the *period of responsibility* argument, to which a brief reference should be made. It is usually the case that the maximum period over which a politician or an engineer carries great responsibilities is about a generation, or, say, thirty years. Now during this period of time a coastal problem may be shelved by the usual processes of looking the other way, calling for reports, or pleading lack of funds; or, alternatively, it may be dealt with by building a structure which in the long term may be a waste of money and effort, but which is likely to survive for the vital span of thirty years, and so seemingly do credit to its authors during their periods of responsibility if not for the rest of their lives. It is not difficult in these days to build sea defences which will last thirty years. But what good has been done if at the end of that time the general rate of erosion has not been halted? It would be possible to point to a number of minor defence schemes whose usefulness has been negligible, and to some large ones which, in the long run, have been of little value. What is of vital importance is that there shall be a thorough examination of each particular problem, and the best possible long-term solution of it determined, taking into account the economic factors as far as they can be assessed at the time.

What I have attempted is a very brief treatment of coastal changes. First the implications of material are considered, especially their reactions to the more important processes to which they are subjected. Next the processes themselves are discussed, and following this a brief examination of how far existing forms can be explained in terms of these two factors. It is at this stage that the complexities of the problem appear. The chapter on 'Methods of Observation' makes clear I hope that changes which are taking place before our eyes are still imperfectly understood, for reasons which are easy to appreciate. They take place in conditions where there are many unknowns, that is, in the surf zone. Wave behaviour is well understood by the mathematicians except that, so far, they have been unable to deal with the breaking wave. In this book I have quoted some invaluable mathematics concerning wave behaviour, but it all stops short at the plunge line, or where the surf begins. Observers and experimenters are limited in almost the same way. Much of the mathematical theory has been confirmed by observation either in nature or in the laboratories. But once the surf begins observation becomes difficult and uncertainties increase. These limitations are most unfortunate, for it is precisely in the surf, in this defiant difficult area that the rapid and important changes are taking place. Recently developed techniques inspire hope for the future, and there is hope that soon the laboratories, furnished with more reliable observations from the beaches, will solve problems which at present baffle us.

And if changes which are taking place now cannot be explained, how much more difficult it is to explain formations which were fashioned in the geological past. It is possible to make intelligent guesses that might explain some of them in terms of processes which we know to be in operation today. Others demand assumptions of other kinds of which earth movements are probably the outstanding example. Here our difficulties increase; primarily because we know so little about the movements in detail, how great, and how rapid they were. But even if the exact history of these movements were known in detail our difficulties would probably not be solved. It would be difficult, though perhaps not impossible, to simulate in the laboratory a process which involves waves whose periods are measured in seconds, tides whose movements are reckoned in hours, and vertical land and water oscillations which continued for thousands of years, besides problems of changing climates and current actions. In such circumstances it is not surprising to find one worker in this field sceptical about the ideas of others; certainly I cannot always be dogmatic about my own.

As I send this manuscript to the publishers I have a feeling that it asks more questions than it answers, and readers may consider this an unsatisfactory state of affairs. Unfortunately in this field it is inevitable; it would be quite misleading to leave readers with the impression that problems are understood when it is abundantly clear that they are not. I hope that in the following pages I have at least distinguished between what is clearly known and what is fondly believed.

It is with pleasure that I record my association with many who, while sharing no responsibility for the defects of this book, have stimulated my interest and contributed to whatever merit it may have. Frank Debenham, Emeritus Professor of Geography at Cambridge University, many years ago inaugurated the small hydraulic laboratory in the department where I am employed and began the systematic study of present coastal changes. I shall ever be grateful to him for his wise counsels and his most cheerful encouragement. His successor, Professor Steers, whose considerable work in this field is well known, has continued to give help, encouragement and advice. I am indebted, too, to my colleague Mr. W. V. Lewis, to my former pupil and collaborator Miss (Dr.) Cuchlaine King, to Commander D. H. Fryer, with whom I worked extensively during the war and since; he has displayed more practical knowledge and sound sense about beaches than most of the pundits, and with Mr. Roger Smith, fisherman of Southwold, has never let me stray from realities. I have valued my association with Professor Jacques Bourcart of the Sorbonne, and with Dr. Martin A. Mason and Dr. G. H. Keulegan, formerly of the Beach Erosion Board, Washington. I am indebted to the U.S. Hydrographic Office for permission to reproduce appendices from their publication H.O. Pub. 601, *Wind, Sea and Swell: Theory of Relations for Forecasting*, by H. U. Sverdrup and W. H. Munk, and to Dr. Munk himself for permission to quote from his work. Grants from the Royal Society and the Nature Conservancy have made it possible to carry out research in the South of France and on our East Coast. I remember with great pleasure the co-operation of my small unit during the war, No. 2 Air Survey Liaison Section R.E., my family and friends and students who have helped me with observations in circumstances which have always been congenial and amusing, if not always comfortable. I suspect that such of them as see this book will regard it as a trivial outcome of their sufferings.

Cambridge   W. W. W.
June 1959

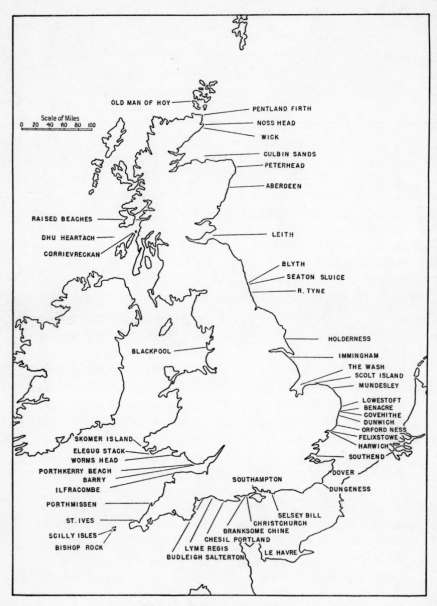

Map labels:

OLD MAN OF HOY
PENTLAND FIRTH
NOSS HEAD
WICK
CULBIN SANDS
PETERHEAD
ABERDEEN
RAISED BEACHES
DHU HEARTACH
CORRIEVRECKAN
LEITH
BLYTH
SEATON SLUICE
R. TYNE
HOLDERNESS
IMMINGHAM
THE WASH
SCOLT ISLAND
MUNDESLEY
BLACKPOOL
LOWESTOFT
BENACRE
COVEHITHE
DUNWICH
ORFORD NESS
FELIXSTOWE
HARWICH
SOUTHEND
SKOMER ISLAND
ELEGUG STACK
WORMS HEAD
PORTHKERRY BEACH
BARRY
ILFRACOMBE
DOVER
DUNGENESS
SOUTHAMPTON
PORTHMISSEN
ST. IVES
SELSEY BILL
CHRISTCHURCH
BRANKSOME CHINE
CHESIL PORTLAND
LYME REGIS
BUDLEIGH SALTERTON
LE HAVRE
SCILLY ISLES
BISHOP ROCK

Scale of Miles
0 20 40 60 80 100

MAP OF ENGLAND AND WALES

CHAPTER I

THE GENERAL PROBLEM

DURING the war of 1939–45 it was decided to mount an amphibious operation on the beaches of Salerno Bay in Italy. The largest landing craft employed had a draught of about 10 feet, and it was predicted that the clearance over the sandbar which was known to exist along the length of the bay was greater than this, so that it would not impede the craft. The prediction was justified, for on 9 September 1945 the landing craft safely cleared the bar. But two days later, in what appeared to be similar conditions, the craft stuck on the bar. What had happened? The difficulty could not be explained by a drop in sea level due to the tides, which in this part of the world are always small. The fact was that in forty-eight hours this large fringing sandbar had moved or grown so that the amount of water over it was reduced from 10 feet to—probably 8½ feet.

This small change was noticed because it almost wrecked a difficult and hazardous military operation. Little was known about the offshore bar in those days; yet the phenomenon should have surprised no one, for change is the very essence of the coastal zone. This is obvious to the casual holiday-maker who sits in front of the sea wall at a fashionable seaside resort; it is infinitely more apparent to those who make a systematic study of coastlines which are unprotected by artificial structures.

Between the spells of monsoon rain in Ceylon the mouths of large rivers in the dry zone are closed by

I

sandbanks which form rapidly so as to make a continuous coastline. In Suffolk the soft cliffs are eroded so fast that a churchyard, in use during the last century, is falling into the sea; the Church of Eccles in Norfolk, which in 1869 was standing in the dunes, is now so low on the beach that it can be seen only at low tide. Again, we can see old beaches and marine caves in the Western Highlands of Scotland many feet high on the hillside, while at Blyth in Northumberland tree-stumps on the beach are clear evidence that the sea has invaded what was formerly forest. The sandbanks off Lowestoft move so fast that it is necessary to survey them almost annually in order that the navigable channels can be properly marked by buoys. These are a few examples of changes which are all too apparent to a careful observer and which demonstrate quite clearly that the division between land and sea is not something permanent and immutable, but a zone varying in size, configuration and position.

Of course it could not be otherwise; it is difficult to think of a single factor in coastlines and coastal behaviour which does not in some way undergo considerable change. Think of the wind varying from the calm of a day when not even a leaf is stirred to the violence of a hurricane when the air is full of sand or spray. And it is this wind which generates the waves; waves which on a calm day are non-existent—or at least imperceptible— but which at their fiercest are able to break sea walls, to hurl ships on to the rocks, or pieces of shingle scores of feet into the air to the tops of lighthouses. There is an infinite variation in wave patterns—in their heights, lengths and directions; sometimes they take the form of an oily swell, at other times roaring breakers; and, as if that were not enough, these patterns can be bent by the sea bed or reflected by the shore or be superimposed one upon another to form a sea which is rightly called 'wild' and 'confused'.

But we have hardly begun our catalogue of change. The sea level rises and falls under tidal action by amounts which are very inconstant; and sometimes, as in the North Sea for instance, there are freak rises and falls, known as 'surges', which are the result of meteorological causes which are less predictable than the astronomical factors which account for ordinary tides. Tidal rises and falls are accompanied by tidal streams, not to be confused with ocean currents, though both may be responsible for transporting beach materials from place to place.

The sea varies in temperature and salinity, and therefore in density, and these variations in density are of great importance in a study of the circulation of water in the oceans.

Most of the changes mentioned so far can within certain limits be observed and measured; but it is important that these 'limitations' should be mentioned, for, as will appear later, some very obvious difficulties are encountered by the oceanographer who works on the edge of the sea. How is he to mount his instruments or make his observations? In the surf zone where his interest is greatest the water is too shallow for large ships and too rough for small boats; 'breakers' are the dread of every sailor and yet it is among the breakers that the work of moulding—by erosion or deposition—is going on. It is a tantalizing thought that it is easier to measure ocean currents and wave heights in mid-ocean than in water less than 20 feet deep. Estimates can be made, but the estimates may often be rough and misleading.

Other changes occur which are difficult to measure, and no better instance of this can be quoted than the variations in sea level over long periods or the vertical movements of land masses. A former beach high on a hillside, or a former land feature now submerged may be explained either because the land has risen or fallen, or

3

because the mean level of the sea has moved in the opposite sense. Both land and sea levels are known to undergo secular changes; earth movements are well known to the geographers, and the melting of polar ice-caps has a well-known effect on the depths of the seas; what is not so easy to understand is whether an anomaly such as a raised beach is caused by an uplift of the land, a fall in sea level, or both, or indeed how many such vertical oscillations have taken place.

These forces and movements then are very erratic; but we must now consider the substance of the coastline; here we find that its resistance is extremely variable. The fringing sea may in rare cases act upon mud; frequently upon sand, upon shingle banks, or upon cliffs whose consistency varies from the loose sand of Dunwich to the hard resistant granite of Land's End. Even the hard rocks behave differently according to their composition and jointing; the granite of the Cornish coast is extremely resistant; the Needles, like Fingal's cave or the limestone arches of South-east Sicily, owe their forms to the characteristic jointing of the rocks of which they are composed.

If we are to understand the almost infinite variety of coastal forms that we may encounter in our travels, we must bear in mind all these factors, for what we see is the result of the interplay between some, and probably many, of them.

Coastlines thus possess an infinite variety of geological formations which are worked upon by agencies almost equally varied and numerous. If cliffs give an impression of permanence, this impression may be justified in parts of Cornwall, where the hardness of the rocks prevents the sea from encroaching at any great speed. But, unfortunately, not all cliffs are so hard and on our south and east coasts are many places where cliffs of sand, chalk, and clay are receding very fast indeed. It must also be remembered that if the sea at a given time is eroding a beach of sand or shingle, some slight change in the action of the sea might at any given time cause erosion to give place to deposition; but this reconstruction can hardly happen to cliffs. The sea working at their feet may cause them to fall; it can never replace material at the top of them.

Our coast may consist of shingle. Usually shingle is derived from fallen cliffs; at first it is angular; later it becomes rounded and reduced in size, the rate of reduction depending upon the hardness of the fragments and the violence and duration of the wave action. Chalk fragments are quickly broken down; flint fragments have a long life. We speak of the 'nourishment' of shingle banks or beaches, and this means quite simply that material has arrived on the beach from wherever the source may be. If there is no nourishment of a shingle feature it must be reduced in size because there must be a gradual reduction in the size of the constituent particles. If the rate of nourishment is greater than the rate of attrition the formation will increase in size; if it is less a gradual reduction must take place. Chesil beach, which is not augmented, is shrinking; on the other hand Dungeness has grown in historical times because of the accession of material from outside sources.

Sand is proverbially associated with instability, but the association stops at beaches of sand, for these are probably more permanent than any other form of coastline; their gradients are such that the incident waves are gradually robbed of their energy as they run up the beach, and the sand itself is almost indestructible. When a beach is attacked by waves the sand is stirred up and either it settles down in its original position, or if it is transported elsewhere it is replaced by other sand which has been moved thither by the same processes. Bars may be formed, or a succession of small bars, known as bar and runnel, may be a feature of the beach. These move; they may be obliterated for a time, but they are likely to reappear at a later stage; and if the general configuration suffers any permanent change it is likely to be very slow.

But if the general form, the plan and profile of sand beaches, are relatively stable, it must not be supposed that sand features are lacking in variety or change. I have already referred to bars, and in Chapter V where their variety and behaviour is discussed, it is shown that they are the cause of great irregularity in the relief of the sea bed within the breaker zone. Features like tombolos, the haffs of the Baltic, and the lagoon bars on the French Mediterranean coast are particular cases of the end product of wave and current action on freely moving material, while the patterns of beach cusps and ripples vary from hour to hour.

The catalogue is unending; even the mud in marshes and backwaters changes, though perhaps not as fast as the cliffs and shingle. But we shall see that the gradual augmentation of marsh levels is followed by colonization by marsh plants; the level then rises, and a small piece of what was sea is ready for reclamation.

And landward of the beach there may be dunes; the measure of their permanence is the flying sand when the wind is strong enough to move it. If the dunes are well planted with marram or other vegetation they may remain undisturbed for a time; but often they come and go with remarkable speed.

These, then, are examples of changing coastlines, and our aim is to consider the changes, to assess their importance, and, if possible, to seek their causes. To those who watch the waves and the sea, the beaches and shingle banks, an endless succession of questions comes to mind. To many of these questions the answers have not yet been found; many of the answers given hitherto have

6

been inadequate or misleading. A proper understanding will be reached only after an infinite amount of observations and research.

Our present ignorance is not surprising, for the problem takes us to the fringe of many sciences. It cannot be solved without help from the geologist, the meteorologist, the hydraulic engineer and the mathematician. The individual genius with a mastery in all of these fields and an enthusiasm for the subject has not yet been born, and it is because of the width of the problem that it has attracted the attention of geographers whose range of interest has led them to do some most valuable work. The engineers who have had the greatest responsibility in the matter have suffered from the fact that their masters have given them a series of difficult and localized problems with inadequate resources for solving them, so that their efforts have been all too often confined to the temporary repair of local damage with little regard to its cause or to the possible unfortunate consequences of their own cure.

For the first quarter of this century, then, the problem had been dealt with in width by workers such as Johnson, Davis, Vaughan Cornish, Sheppard, Steers and Bourcart, and in detail by a number of engineers whose work, which calls for the highest praise, suffered from being what may be described as *ad hoc*.

Our national apathy to the problem has been slightly removed by the character of the war of 1939–45, in which beach landings and therefore beach problems in general were of great importance; and by the disastrous storm of 1953, and the resultant activities of the Waverley Committee. Unfortunately there are signs that the former neglect may reassert itself; few of our beaches are free from the risk of pollution by sewage; some are used for dumping slag from coal-mines. Until we have a national pride in our coastal fringe, it is not to be

7

expected that private individuals and public bodies will concern themselves with matters which do not make obvious urgent demands on their purses.

But in this country two important developments have taken place which provide grounds for hope; these are the founding of a National Institute of Oceanography and independently a Department of Hydraulics Research. Both are manned by scientists well able to address themselves to the problem. Unfortunately their resources are limited and the coastal problem is so large and so varied that it would be unreasonable to suppose that sensational progress will be achieved. It is gratifying, however, that two such departments have at last been brought into being, and that the country has taken up the challenge of the encircling sea.

CHAPTER II

THE GEOLOGICAL BACKGROUND

THE configuration of a coastline must obviously be determined by two main factors; the nature of the geological formation in which it lies and the kind of modifying processes to which it is subjected. Both are important. If a coastline consists of hard rock it will be changed very slowly; if it is soft it may undergo rapid change. And yet it is not as simple as this, for beaches of sand, though subject to short time changes, can retain a remarkably constant form as long as they are adequately secured at either end. The fact that the sand is very mobile means that if it is quickly removed it may in favourable circumstances be quickly replaced. It is important therefore to consider how far the form and behaviour of a coastline is governed by its geology; by this is meant both the nature of the parent rock and the configuration into which it was moulded before the marine processes began.

The general outlines of many coastal features have been little affected by marine agencies; for instance, the resistant rocky coasts of Western Scotland owe their outlines (save for the effect of submergence which will be dealt with later) to the very early mountain-forming processes and subsequent glacial action. The sea has had comparatively little effect in a broad sense, though the effect of its work in detail will be apparent.

It is convenient to begin a study of coastal forms with cliffs. It may appear at first sight that there could be no better defence against the sea than cliffs; but this view would not be shared by many house-owners on our east and south coasts. Cliffs of hard rock are of course only very slowly affected by wave action; the granite at Land's End and the schists at Start Point are instances of rocks which are subject to the fiercest action of the sea but which show little signs of retreat. It is doubtful whether the action of the sea will have a measurable effect on the granite stump of Ailsa Craig in historical time. Sometimes hard rocks appear to be vulnerable at the joints, and the evidence of erosion can be seen, but the attrition of pebbles and the effect of pressure in the fissures are very slow processes, and, by comparison with other kinds of coastline, the rates of change are negligible.

There are some cliffs of rock which appear at first sight to be hard which, in fact, bear distinct signs of erosion. The best examples are those rocks which are soluble in water and whose joints are vulnerable to the pressure built up by wave action. Chalk, limestone, the sandstones and the schists provide the best instances, and in this country the 'White Cliffs of Dover', The Needles, and the arches of Flamborough Head are well-known examples of the kind of cliff in chalk formations. In Scotland there are many examples of similar erosion in the Old Red Sandstone. Plate I shows spectacular examples in carboniferous limestones and schists. The rocks, being vulnerable at their joints, are broken down at sea level, and being undercut subsequently collapse; the debris is then removed by the action of waves and longshore drifting. Most of the debris is fairly rapidly broken up, and it disappears, save for any hard fragments such as the flints from the chalk, which usually remain in evidence as shingle banks, either at the foot of the cliffs or at some remoter places to which they have been carried by longshore drifting.

The importance of this loosely jointed kind of formation in the general story of coastal erosion is that, assuming the same degree of erosional force, it will retreat faster than the harder cliffs, but not so fast as the very soft cliffs shortly to be discussed. And it is in such cliffs that some of the most spectacular coastal features are to be found.

The form of the cliffs is occasioned by the comparatively loose jointing of the rock. As a result of loosening round these joints by wave action the material falls in

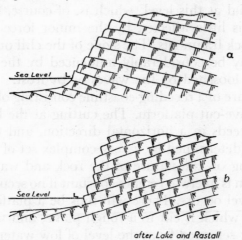

after Lake and Rastall

FIG. II.1.—The effect of dipping strata on cliff formation.

rectangular blocks, causing vertical walls, arches and pinnacles.

It is sometimes argued that the rate of erosion of cliffs is affected by the dip of the strata, since a cliff such as (b) in Fig. II.1 would be more unstable than one like (a). There is little doubt that the *form* of the cliff, that is to say its slope, must be to a large extent governed by the dip of the bedding planes, but it is doubtful whether the rate of recession of the cliffs is much affected by it. What governs the rate of erosion is the rate of cutting back at L and it is difficult to understand how this can be affected by minor variations in the dip of the rock. The force of gravity is negligible compared with the force exerted by the waves as they break.

Measurements made at these levels have shown that hydraulic pressures up to 5,000 to 6,000 lb. per square foot may occur. It is this force, along with the inevitable abrasion which loosens particles of the cliff. What happens to the rocks then depends upon local conditions of current and wave transport. Thus the rate of removal of material at this level, which is, of course, the rate of erosion, is little affected by the minor force of gravity on the rock fragments. The slope of the cliff on the other hand may be considerably influenced by the sliding of particles loosened by the waves or by frost.

A feature of a receding coastline consisting of hard rock is the wave-cut platform. The cutting at the base of the cliff proceeds in a horizontal direction, and to a depth which is determined by a very complex set of conditions depending on the nature of the rock and wave pattern but which is likely to remain constant if no secular change in sea level occurs. There will thus be a platform below the cliffs which is cut to a rough plane, and whose level is not far removed from the level of low water. The rate of construction of a wave-cut platform must proceed at a diminishing speed; to seaward of the platform there is likely to be a terrace of the debris, so that the wave energy will be dissipated over a gradually widening band of shallow water; and the assault at the foot of the cliff must therefore be diminished as the width of the platform and terrace increases. There are excellent examples of wave-cut platforms at the foot of the chalk cliffs in Sussex. They are to be regarded as evidence of the recession of the cliffs, and in so far as they cause a dissipation of wave action they undoubtedly have the effect of reducing the rate of erosion of the cliffs themselves.

Some cliff coastlines are very impermanent, and some of the most sensational changes in our coastline occur in areas where the sea is fronted by cliffs of soft sand, gravel or boulder clay. Such cliffs form a large part of the East Coast of England, those at Dunwich, Southwold, Mundesley and Holderness being well-known examples. Their very softness makes them vulnerable to water action of any kind. When the waves cut at the base the face grows steeper until the angle of rest of the material is exceeded, when the cliff collapses. Cliffs consisting, either wholly or partly, of clay become unstable because they tend to slide along joints into which drainage water has found its way. At Covehithe, where the cliffs consist of glacial sand with only a little gravel, the normal angle of rest is about 45°. Sometimes erosion by the sea is such that the angle becomes about 70°, but it is at this stage that the cliff becomes unstable and falls occur. It is only because of a most unfortunate combination of circumstances that these falls are important, because if the fallen material were subsequently to be spread over the foreshore and beach—which is the real protective belt against the action of the sea—it would have the effect of holding the sea back. But at Covehithe and at other places on the East Coast the material from cliff falls does not stay where it has fallen, or on the beach immediately fronting it; it is rapidly removed laterally and seaward leaving the beach denuded so that the cliff is open to the assault of the waves during the next storm.

The process described above is clearly one of erosion; and no better example of a coastline which is in retreat could be found. Sometimes some slight change in local conditions can modify the action of currents and wave patterns so that—temporarily at least—the balance is redressed, and material which has been eroded is brought back again. Such changes are rare, it is true; and when they do occur they must be confined to the foreshore where the waves and currents are at work; but the cliffs themselves cannot be replaced in this way, for waves never reach the upper levels of cliff formations. It should therefore be remembered that a retreating cliff line represents an irreplaceable loss *at that place*. The eroded material may of course be subsequently deposited elsewhere. Dungeness has already been quoted as an example of a feature whose constituent material is derived from erosion at other places.

Between the cliffs and the headlands are often what are known as beaches; these consist of long inclined planes of unconsolidated, freely moving material, material of which we shall consider three kinds; shingle, sand and mud. A beach may consist entirely of shingle or sand. For reasons that will be seen later mud is less likely to be found on open beaches, though it is occasionally found: but where it does exist it is usually not seen on the surface, but is at a level below the sand surface. The commonest beach materials, however, are shingle and sand, and these are frequently to be found on the same beach; but the two materials are sorted either horizontally or vertically.

Sorting of Beach Materials

The processes responsible for sorting and grading beach materials are extremely complex, and are not fully understood, so that it is possible to discuss them only in the most general terms. It is hoped that future investigators will be able to throw more light on what is an interesting and important problem. It is, however, possible to point to a number of ways in which beach material can be sorted, usually in terms of particle size. A more detailed treatment of settling velocities is given later, pp. 19 and 20; but anyone bathing in the sea on a rough day can observe for himself that whereas small grains of material may be comparatively easily raised into suspension, others, such as large stones, need a much greater effort. And further, while the latter, once raised from the sea bed will quickly sink back again, the former will subside very slowly. Table I on p. 20 shows the velocities that are required to move material of different sizes; it is easy to see from this table that if the water velocity were 90 cm. per second, coarse sand and particles up to a median diameter of 8 mm. would be removed, while particles of 10 mm. and greater would remain; and the same sorting or separation will occur at other velocities. If, therefore, the water velocities on the beach vary, it is to be expected that bands of differing material sizes may be found on beaches. We shall see later that widely differing water velocities are found in the waves that break on a beach; for instance, before the waves have broken the water particles move quite slowly, but in the smallest breakers the movement is almost violent. Thus banding or sorting must take place, and the results of this will doubtless have been seen by every reader of this book.

Shingle ridges are evidence of this sorting process, but probably the commonest result of it is to be seen on beaches of both shingle and sand where the shingle is on the higher levels of the beach, while the lower levels are sand. This is almost invariably the case. Chesil beach is an exception because the supply of shingle is so great that it continues well below the level of low water springs, and far into the bay. But the exceptions are few, and shingle frequently exists as a narrow strip at the top of a beach which is predominantly sand.

The shingle at the very top of a beach is placed there by the action of very large breakers which occur very rarely; they are transported with the 'exploding' water of breakers, and not by the general flow of the sea. For this reason the disposition of shingle at the top levels, especially in groynes, is often an unreliable indicator of the movement of material on the beach as a whole, because it is freak material at a freak level. It is easy to watch the movement of the shingle, a fast-moving material, at the upper limit of wave action, but it must be remembered that quantitatively the important changes take place at the lower levels. It has frequently been observed that the disposition of shingle at the top level of groynes has suggested coastwise movement in a direction exactly opposite to the one prevailing.

The kind of sorting mentioned above may be called *horizontal* sorting. There must also be vertical sorting.

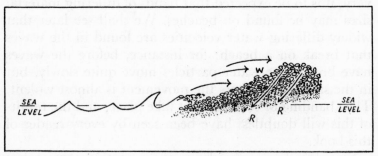

FIG. II.2.—Vertical sorting with shingle as a top layer.

Let us consider the effect of the impact of waves on a shingle bank, assuming that the waves have raised shingle, sand, and even finer particles of mud into suspension. The wave strikes the beach at W carrying the mixed material with it (Fig. II.2). The shingle face acts as a sieve. The coarse material is retained in the sieve, and the smaller ones fall through as the water returns in the direction R. Then the sand, in time, will pass through the fine shingle, and the mud through the sand. It must be said at once that Fig. II.2 is to some extent a simplified concept: but it explains in general why shingle overlies sand, and why mud, if it is found on beaches at all, is found under sand. In 1945, at Morib in Malaya, there was a disastrous military landing

because so-called intelligence officers could not be per-
suaded to believe that a well-known sandy bathing
beach consisted mainly of mud. It is hoped that the
disappearance of tanks and lorries in the mud on D-Day
has removed what was a dangerous and expensive mis-
conception. The most attractive expanse of golden sand
may consist of only a thin layer of interlocking fragments
overlying finer material.

Mud, happily for holiday-makers, does not often
appear as a beach material. Vertical sorting has already
been dealt with, but very fine material is removed from
beaches by other means. Wheeler makes the remarkable
statement, 'Alluvium derived from the erosion of sea
cliffs is never drifted along the beach in the same way
that shingle and sand are,' and then goes on to argue a
gradual diffusion of suspended material, and ultimate
deposition in, 'A depth where there is no longer any
agitation from the waves'. After the observation that 'As
a rule, the water of the sea is clear and transparent near
the shore', is an apparently contradictory 'Close to the
shores during onshore gales . . . the water becomes
charged with solid matter, rendering it turbid . . . but
this appearance does not extend far from the land. . . .'
Such remarks help very little.

A feature of the North Sea is that, at least South of
the Wash it is nearly always turbid inshore. Wave action
gets the fine material into suspension and it drifts. The
water circulation is such that some of the muds and
alluvia find their way to deep water and stay there, but
it would seem that there is another very simple disposition of muds which is in fact a process of sorting.
Let us assume that a sea, drifting along the coast, has
mud in suspension. It is held in suspension by wave
action. When the tide flows into the estuaries and inlets—
including the marshes—the mud, in suspension, goes
with it. But here, in the sheltered water, the turbulence

is very small by comparison with the open sea, and the mud particles have time to settle. On the ebb, the water debouches into the sea *minus* the load of mud that it brought in. Hence the muddy estuaries and the growth of mud flats.

Mud brought down to the estuaries or mud flats by rivers (as distinct from that brought in from the sea) would be deposited due to the same mechanical process. But there is also an additional factor which would make for a more complete deposition of river mud particles. When the particles in suspension in fresh water encounter the brine at the sea water/fresh water interface an electro-chemical action is set up which tends to precipitate the colloidal muds. Thus the muds deposited from riverine sources are likely to be finer than those which have been brought in from the sea. The difference is not likely to be very apparent, since they must be thoroughly mixed.

Mud, then, is a rare but by no means unknown constituent of open beaches. It has been argued by those who wish to dump coal ash and coal waste on beaches that fine material *cannot* stay on beaches, since it is not a 'beach-forming material'. Quite obviously it will stay there until it is taken away. Usually the process of removal is quite rapid with the result that sand beaches are clean. If, however, the rate of deposition is greater than the rate of removal, it is obvious that some fine material will remain on the beach.

Particle Sizes and Settling Velocities, etc.

Before dealing with the features of shingle, sand and mud it is well to consider in greater detail how the particles of materials of various sizes behave when moved by water. The densities of the particles are of less importance than their sizes; granite and flint have specific gravities or densities of about 2·7, whilst what are known as heavy rocks, such as the basalts, have densities of 2·9–3·0. The effect of particle size, however, is of the greatest importance.

Writers on coastal phenomena often fall into the error of using the argument of river and irrigation channel engineers when dealing with the problem of the transport of material. While the results attained by such authorities are of the greatest importance in their own field it must not be forgotten that there is a fundamental difference between the two problems. In rivers the movement of material can be caused only by the *flow* of the water, either laminar or turbulent; that is to say the capacity of the stream to move material is dependent upon the *prior* requirement of picking it up. This is not so in the marine problem; here we must assume the material to be stirred in suspension by wave action, and that once it is raised from the bottom it can be influenced by current flow.

The point will probably be made clearer by quoting from two tables, one from Hjulström [1] and the other from Wheeler [1]. The materials quoted in Table I on the following page are selected from thirty-two examples given in the original table.

This table points to the obvious conclusion that the larger the particle the larger must be the water velocity required to move it, down to a median diameter of 0·4 mm., at which stage the converse appears to hold. And it is at this end of the table that caution is needed. It is easy to see that a river bed of clay will need a bigger eroding force than a bed of sand; but this assumes that the clay particles are compacted. Particles of comparable size, in problems of sea erosion, are usually brought down by rivers, and so are already in suspension, or, if they have been on the beach for a time, have not been there long enough to form a consolidated homogeneous whole.

Kind of material	Diameter of particles	Velocity required for erosion	Remarks
	mm.	cm. per sec.	
Stiff Clay	0·0015	130	Some mean grain diameters for
Alluvial Silt	0·005	76	sand given by Dr. C. A. M.
Quicksand	0·13	27	King [2] are
Sand	0·40	15	Blackpool 0·22 mm.
Sand	0·70	20	Rhossili 0·23 ,,
Coarse Sand	1·71	34	Whitbeck 0·29 ,,
	4·0	49	Holme (Norfolk) 0·31 ,,
	8·0	81	0·41 bottom of
	16·0	130–180	Druridge beach
	50·0	238	0·80 top of beach
	70·0	266–280	

TABLE I.

(After Hjulström [1].)

For our purposes Hjulström's table, which at its lower end is of great interest to us, needs supplementing by a table of the kind given by Wheeler [1][1] (see Table II).

Material	Grain size	Time taken to settle 10 inches	Settling Velocity
	mm.		ft. per minute
Small Pebbles	5	1 sec.	50
Coarse Sand	1·25	2¼ sec.	22
Sand	0·25	10 sec.	5
Silt	0·05	2 m. 0 sec.	0·42
Fine Alluvium	0·0125	28 m.	0·03

TABLE II. SETTLING VELOCITIES OF BEACH MATERIALS.

(Modified from Wheeler.)

[1] There are obvious mistakes in Wheeler's table which I have corrected in Table II.

20

The results came from the comparatively simple experiment of timing the rate of fall of particles of various sizes in a large tube, over a vertical distance of 10 inches. The results are probably approximate because of the shortness of the drop, but they are of great interest and importance.

Let us consider the behaviour of the largest particle mentioned in this table, the small pebble about ¼ inch in diameter. We know from experience that in waves 6 feet high, whose period we can assume to be eight seconds, surf particles are raised to the surface at the point where the waves break. A particle so raised to the surface in water 6 feet deep settling at a rate of 50 feet per minute would no sooner have reached the bottom, than the succeeding wave would stir it into suspension again, though possibly not right to the surface. Thus it would be constantly under the influence of whatever current might be running. The example is perhaps an over-simplification of what happens, especially since it ignores the complications of movement in very turbulent water, but it does at least demonstrate how great a load of material of comparatively large particles may be in suspension, and therefore subject to current action almost continuously during storms. The table also demonstrates how large particles subside more quickly than small ones, and how persistent is the suspension of grains of silt and sand in moderate wave action.

Shingle

Shingle is quite simply gravel or stone fragments; the term is applied to such stones on a beach; it is sometimes used for clean gravel which is found inland. The behaviour of shingle on a beach is governed by wave and current action, and by the rate of settling, all of which have been discussed earlier. The interplay of these factors, both horizontally and vertically, results in a process so complex and so rapid that observation is difficult, and the interpretation of the observation is obscure.[1]

Shingle is usually derived from neighbouring rock formations; much of it consists of flints from chalk cliffs or hard fragments of carboniferous limestone or other rocks. The essential property is hardness; soft rocks are quickly broken up under wave action and do not survive to form shingle features.

The sorting into banks has already been explained. Another feature of shingle beaches is the ridges which form very rapidly, but which are equally rapidly destroyed and replaced by successive ridges at slightly different places and of different sizes. Ridges seem to be formed at the stand of high tides when particles are projected upwards by incoming waves, and the forward slope is combed down as the waves recede. Thus, as the tidal range falls from springs and neaps, a succession of ridges may be left. The features, which are very ephemeral, are of some interest, but of little importance. The gradient of shingle on ridges may be as steep as 1 in 1, though small rounded particles may sometimes form as gentle a slope as 1 in 10. On shingle beaches as a whole gradients of 1 in 4 are quite common. When the material consists of newly derived, and therefore un-rounded fragments, it can be packed very firmly, almost like bricks. In such circumstances the angle of slope may be quite steep.

There is an excellent example of the beginning, life, and almost decay of a shingle beach at Porthkerry, near Barry, in South Wales, and probably nothing can better demonstrate what shingle is, and how it behaves, than a brief description of what is seen there. The resultant[2]

---

[1] There is no reason why this obscurity should continue; large wave tanks and modern photographic methods could provide the clearest evidence of how shingle behaves.

[2] I use resultant drift to mean what is left when the differing effects of ebb and flow tides and the currents have been taken into account.

drift is from west to east, as is shown in Fig. II.3. Wave action on the cliffs of the lower lias limestone at the Bulwarks, near A, results in considerable falls, and at the foot of the cliffs can be seen angular debris, some fragments of which are sometimes 5 or 6 feet across. This

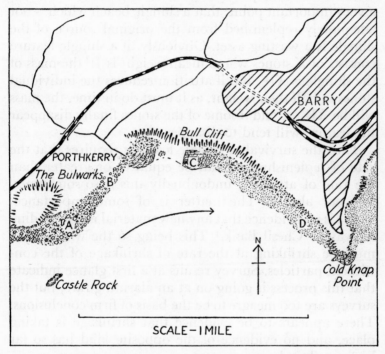

FIG. II.3.—Movement of beach material at Porthkerry.

material is worked on by the waves; it is quickly broken, and, as it is heaved about by the waves, it is chipped and reduced in size, until at the point B the stones are about the size of a man's head and have rounded edges, though their original rectangular form is still in evidence. At C the stones are further reduced in size and their mean is about the size of a brick, but the flat sides have gone, and the stones are ellipsoidal in form. At D such stones as remain are quite small—about as big as hens' eggs—and it is noticeable that whereas at A and B the beach appears to consist entirely of stones, all that remains at D is a strip of shingle at the top of the beach. The lower part of it is sand.

This brief description of a well-known beach illustrates a very important point; that a shingle beach which is not adequately replenished from the original source of the shingle is a wasting asset. Obviously, if a shingle feature consists of X stones whose mean weight is W the mass of the shingle is XW. But if attrition reduces the individual stones to half their weight, as it must do in time, the mass will be $XW/2$; and if some of the stones finally disappear the feature will tend to disappear too.

Thus the survival of shingle features requires that the rate of replenishment shall be equal to or greater than the rate of attrition; undoubtedly this is so sometimes, but not always. The matter is of some importance. There is no evidence that any new material is now finding its way to Chesil Bank.[1] This being so the whole bank must be shrinking at the rate of shrinkage of the constituent particles. Survey results at a first glance indicate that this process is going on at an alarming rate, but the surveys are too meagre to be the basis of firm conclusions. There appears to be evidence that shrinkage is taking place, and no evidence of the opposite kind has so far been produced.

The behaviour of some shingle features is discussed in Chapter V.

[1] At a public enquiry in Dorset on 14/15 December 1955 it was claimed that 'sub-angular' material was carried from the Triassic pebble beds in the neighbourhood of Budleigh Salterton and Chesil Beach. Dr. Arkell has expressed the opinion that transport from such a source could have taken place at the beginning of the neolithic subsidence. It is difficult to believe that it could occur now, and indeed there is no evidence that it is taking place.

Sand

The geologists apply the name 'sand' to 'loose incoherent aggregates of mineral particles of sufficient size to be easily visible to the naked eye [Lake and Rastall].' They would, however, include finely comminuted pieces of shells. The most common material is quartz, which because of its hardness is most resistant to weathering agents.

In studying coastal behaviour the property of sand chiefly to be borne in mind is grain size. The reader will doubtless have observed that grain sizes vary widely; coarse grains are about 0·02 inches in diameter; fine sand grains could have a diameter of about 0·005 inches; 0·01 inch may be regarded as a mean (see p. 20).

On the beach to the north of Seaton Sluice in Northumberland the grain sizes of the sand vary rapidly in a north–south direction, as well as in a sense at right angles to the coastline. The contractors who sell sand are well aware of this, and they go to different parts of the beach in order to get the grade of sand that the particular customer requires.

It is sometimes said that sand grains at a given place have reached an irreducible size; that is to say, that they are so small that their relative movements in water can never be violent enough to chip off any more pieces. This is an overstatement; it may be nearly true for the hard fragments of quartz or zircon, but it is certainly not true for pieces of softer material such as shell fragments. On the other hand it appears to be beyond dispute that there is little evidence that sand beaches shrink due to the reduction in particle size as shingle beaches are known to do, yet even this statement must be regarded with suspicion; the amount of shingle at a given place usually has definable limits or its source is clearly limited; this can never be said of sand, which may well extend as

25

a continuum from the top of the beach to the deep sea.

The sources of sand are difficult to determine. It is known to be formed in rivers and deserts, and glacial deposits often include large amounts of sand with or without the addition of gravel. And some sand is doubtless produced by the sea when it breaks down the right kind of geological formation. But the specific question, 'Where does this particular sand come from?' is not always easy to answer. In the North Sea there seems to be a limitless supply of sand as a result of glaciation; not only the beaches surrounding it, but also the bed of the sea bears ample testimony to the fact. With a few notable exceptions there are comparatively few sand beaches on the West Coast of Scotland. Explanations may be attempted, but all are open to doubts, and it appears that while we may assume that North Sea sands are of glacial origin, some Mediterranean sands of desert origin, and others fluvial, we have to say in many cases that we simply do not know the source.

Bagnold recognizes that the bulk of quartz grains, whether existing free or in sandstones, have originated from the disintegration of quartz-bearing rock followed by some other process of mechanical abrasion, but he points out that there is no agreement as to how the grains have been reduced to their present size and shape.

Possible processes are temperature splitting, reduction in size by wind action and the action of ice and water. His summing up is:

'On the evidence available, therefore, it seems reasonable to suppose that the vast majority of the existing sand grains have been reduced, either recently or in long ages past, to something very near to their present size by the action of water and perhaps to a lesser extent by that of ice. From the fact, however, that the grains of fluvial and marine sands are in general sharper and

26

less rounded than those found in desert dunes, it is possible that wind action has an appreciable effect on the *shape* of the grains once they have been reduced to such a size that the wind can move them.'

Sand is obviously extremely mobile; it is quickly raised into suspension during storms (see p. 59), and its rate of subsidence, in terms of wave periods, is slow. And yet sand beaches are, as a rule, permanent, though they may undergo quite drastic changes from time to time; changes follow one another in rapid succession until the original shape of beach is restored. This can best be explained by considering two kinds of beaches, one the short embayed beach between headlands, and the second the long strand such as is to be found near Sète in the South of France, or on the coasts of Italy.

In the first case it is rarely possible for the sand to be carried coastwise round the headlands simply because the currents, passing from headland to headland, have little effect at the heads of the bays. As we shall see in Chapter III wave action by itself cannot take the sand further to seaward than the plunge line. Thus the coast has an apron of almost indestructible sand, which absorbs the shock of the waves perfectly. The waves may raise the sand into suspension; there may be a small generation of heat, but after the storm the sand subsides more or less into the place where it was before it was disturbed.

King [1] has carried out experiments which have shown that under wave action beach sands are disturbed to a depth of about 3 per cent of the wave height, but that the depth increases slightly for coarse sands. The observations were made over one tide. The figure is an interesting one, and is a good indication of the amount of sand that is in suspension at a given time and which, it should be noted, becomes subject to the transporting agencies.

27

On the longer beaches the wave action is similar to that on embayed beaches, but here the currents are likely to move the material along; but if some material is removed from a given place, the agency which took it is likely to have brought a similar amount in its place, so that we have, as it were, a gradual uniform movement of material along the whole beach. This movement has the effect of smoothing out the beach, and of producing the beach curve. If the longshore drift is oscillatory, or reversible, erosion is unlikely to occur; but if there is a one-way trend, then it would appear that erosion must take place. It is a surprising fact, however, that in the Western Mediterranean, where a steady rotation round the perimeter takes place, erosion is not marked, at least in the South of France.

The disappearance of sand from a beach is of course a very serious matter, for then the waves will attack the underlying formations which cannot be so resilient. These may be mud, or rock, the soils of the hinterland, or a sea wall. Whatever it may be it is unlikely to be able to offer so perfect resistance to the waves as sand can do.

The thickness of sand beds on beaches varies considerably both in time and place. As has already been explained there may be appreciable short term movements which of necessity mean that at a given place the thickness of the layer is constantly changing. Frequently the sand layer seems to be quite thin, for more often than not when one digs down a foot or so shells, stones or mud are found. It is perhaps unwise to attempt to give figures for a quantity which varies so widely, but to those who have made no such observations it may be of some help to learn that frequently there is less than a foot of pure sand on that part of a beach regularly covered by the tide, while it is unusual to find a depth of more than 4 or 5 feet.

Sand beaches are much flatter than those of shingle. They are rarely steeper than 1 in 25, while the gradients are sometimes as small as 1 in 200, and in very rare instances 1 in 1,000. The gradients of all beaches depend to some extent upon the nature of the wave action, but the fineness of the material is also an important factor. If the reader will consider for a moment how heaps of shingle, sand, and very fine silt would react to an incoming tide the reason is not far to seek; the shingle heaps would tend to stand in their original form; the fine mud, being quickly raised into suspension and slow to subside, would be spread about in a thin flat layer; while the disposition of the sand would be something between these two. The argument applies to sands of different grain sizes; other things being equal, beaches of coarse sand will be steeper than those of fine sand.

The freak mouldings of beaches into runnels and bars and other configurations will be discussed elsewhere. Of ripples and beach cusps nothing will be said; they present interesting problems, but, as far as is known, they are not important features in the development of major coastal changes, except that the movement of water on the sea bed will be retarded if it is rippled.

Mud

The term mud is here intended to include the materials, finer than sand, which once raised into suspension stay so for minutes rather than seconds, and which, if left undisturbed, form sediments. There is a supply of such material fed to the sea by every stream that enters it; some streams carry large amounts of silt, some of which is deposited near the mouth, sometimes as a delta, sometimes in estuaries or mud flats, but the remainder, the finer material, is carried further afield. Some material of this kind may be derived from the beaches themselves; of this, probably the greater part comes from beds of fine-grained material which were laid down long before the beach reached its existing form. The clay associated with submerged forests will provide a small amount of this material, and the very fine particles from cliff falls would naturally remain in suspension for some time. As has been explained on p. 17 mud is unlikely to settle on exposed beaches long enough to form beaches of mud. A beach of mud must mean that the rate of deposition of mud is faster than the rate of removal, and this can rarely be the case, for the processes of removal are very thorough. The deposition of muds, therefore, is easily explained; either such material travelling coastwise enters and settles in the shelters of estuaries and inlets, or, if a stream brings down material at a rate greater than the coastal processes can remove it, a local beach of mud or even a delta is formed. Any intermediate formation of mud on the coastline would seem of necessity to be either ephemeral or artificial.

There are a few exceptions to this generalization, one being the beaches of mud which are sometimes associated with mangroves. But almost certainly the mud is in a sense comparable with that of a submerged forest, in that it was laid down at a pre-beach stage, and the mangroves have the effect of fixing it.

A most unusual coastal formation of mud is to be found near Civitavecchia a few miles north-west of Rome. Here there is no beach according to the usual patterns— there is of course little tide. The edge of the sea is a small vertical bank, like a river bank, and below this is a gently sloping bottom of a soft clayey material which appears to be derived from basaltic formations inland. Certainly it is a most unusual kind of beach, and no sand or shingle was observed on it when it was visited in 1944.

Shorelines of Emergence and Submergence

So far we have considered sea level in a given locality as a horizontal plane which varies only with the amount of tidal rise and fall. But in terms of geological time the level of the sea varies over a far greater range than this, and many coastal features can be explained only by a consideration of these large variations.

It has already been assumed that orogenic movements have accounted for the main geological features of the coastline since they account for the general configuration of the land mass; and it may here be noted that it is such movements which have raised the summit of Mount Everest, which is formed of a rock which was originally laid down under the sea. But there are other causes for changes in sea level. In Antarctica and on the Greenland ice-cap are large masses of ice which, if melted, would supply enough water to raise the level of the oceans of the world by about 100 feet. It is now well known that, due to small variations in the amount of insolation that the earth receives, such changes have in fact taken place; there are, for instance, unmistakable signs of raised beaches 100 feet above mean sea level on the west coast of Scotland. It is also known that during the Pleistocene ice age, when the Arctic ice-cap extended as far south as England, and when much of Northern Europe and North America were covered by ice, the level of the sea was about 300 feet lower than it is now. A few authorities are of the opinion that even lower levels were reached; though the generally accepted view is that a fall of 300 feet was not exceeded.[1] Conversely, climatic conditions which caused the ice-caps to grow would have the effect of lowering the level of the oceans.

While these exchanges between the ice-caps and the oceans were going on isostatic reactions took place; that

[1] The theory that very low sea levels could help to explain the formation of submarine cañons was rapidly dropped. Some think, too rapidly.

is to say, the formation which had previously supported an ice-cap perhaps 5,000 or 10,000 feet thick, rose, when it was removed and the pressure was released; at the same time the land which became covered by water began to sink under its load.

The rise and fall of the ocean level due to these phenomena are called eustatic changes; the rise and fall of the land as it adjusts itself to an increase or decrease in the load that it carries is called isostatic adjustment. The interrelation is far from simple; partly because isostatic adjustments are slow, and continue long after the load transfer has taken place; but also because the observer, who sees the water rise relative to the land, cannot be certain whether the water has risen—a eustatic change— or whether the land has sunk—an isostatic change. If sufficient observations can be made it is sometimes possible to say quite clearly that a change has been isostatic; for if at different points the vertical movement is different in quantity or sign, it is clear that it is not due to a rise or fall in sea level; this must cause a uniform rate of change. Differing degrees of vertical movement must indicate a tilting of the land mass which must be caused by a *land* movement.

It is this process of ice melting and subsequent vertical movements of the land that explains the changes in Sweden on the Gulf of Bothnia which were first investigated by Celsius and Linnaeus. Early in the eighteenth century Celsius estimated that sea level in southern Sweden was falling at the rate of 40 inches per century. At first he thought that this was evidence of a worldwide lowering of sea level. But subsequent observations in other places have revealed either different rates of emergence of the land or that the movement is in the opposite sense. The North of Norway is known to have risen many hundreds of feet in recent times; the land is rising at Stockholm by about six inches per century, while Scania is sinking. It appears, therefore, that the whole Scandinavian peninsula is being tilted about an axis just south of Stockholm.

This example serves to show the differing effects of a change in water level and a land movement. Clearly, the melting of a polar ice-cap must cause the sea level to be raised by approximately the same amount the world over; but this kind of change cannot exist by itself; the removal of the burden of ice must, locally, result in isostatic readjustments, so that a confused pattern of vertical movements is almost inevitable.

It would be misleading to suppose that all these variations are 'geological' in the sense that they took place in the very distant past, or because the rate of change is so slow as to be unobservable. The drowned valleys or raised beaches that we see today undoubtedly reached—approximately—their present levels many thousands of years ago, but it is not to be assumed that such changes are not taking place now.

Valentin, among others, has recently examined the records of Tide Gauges round Britain, and has obtained some interesting evidence of what appear to be changes in the annual mean heights of sea level as indicated by gauges which are now recording. Before discussing his results it is necessary to understand the general principles and working of a tide gauge. First a well W is built (see Fig. II.4) near the sea and connected to it by a pipe of

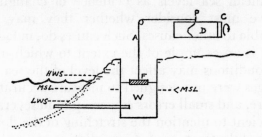

Fig. II.4.—Diagrammatic sketch of a tide gauge.

33

such diameter that wind waves are 'damped' or suppressed while the level of the water in the well is the same as the mean or 'waveless' water level in the open sea. That is to say the tidal wave enters freely but the wind waves which have short periods are suppressed. A float, F, is connected by a wire A, through reduction gearing which is not shown on the diagram, to a pencil P which records on paper mounted on a drum D, which is driven by a 24-hour clock C. The record therefore consists of a series of cosine curves. It will be seen that the position of mean sea level over any period can be deduced from the charts; this may be arrived at in several ways, but it is usually done by computing the mean of hourly heights. This mean 'paper' position clearly corresponds with a position on the side of the well which, in effect, indicates the height of mean sea level.

Subject to certain conditions which we will examine shortly, we should expect the position of the annual mean of sea level for successive years to remain at the same mark on the side of the well. But if the land, and therefore the well, is gradually raised relative to the level of the sea, the M.S.L. mark will appear to be lowered by the same amount. And if, as a result of the melting of snow at the polar ice-caps, the level of the sea rises relative to the land, the annual M.S.L. will appear to rise up the side of the well.

But before we can accept these small variations in annual mean sea levels as evidence of changing base levels, we must consider whether they may not be attributable to other causes. Such causes do, in fact, exist; Fig. II.5 is an example of the extent to which meteorological conditions may affect the level of the sea. Again, tide gauges were not designed to measure accurately to a millimetre, and small errors can creep in in several ways; it is sufficient to mention the stretching of the float wire, corrosion of the float, or an accumulation of weed growth

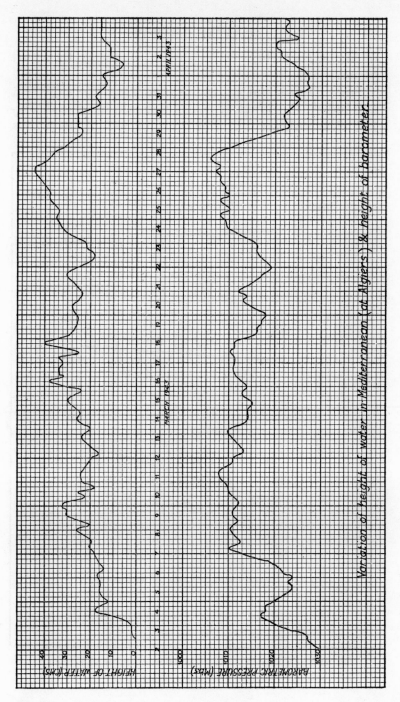

FIG. II.5.—Variation of height of water in Mediterranean (at Algiers) and height of barometer.

on it, or even slight variations in mounting the chart paper.

Small, accidental variations then are to be expected, and indeed this is exactly what Valentin has found. Fig. II.6 clearly shows this. The thin line joining black dots

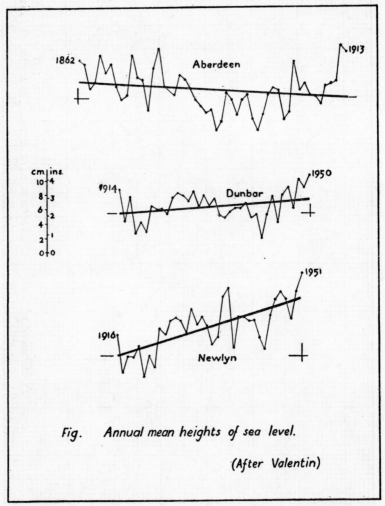

Fig.   Annual mean heights of sea level.

(After Valentin)

FIG. II.6.—Tide level trends at Aberdeen, Dunbar and Newlyn.

rises and falls no doubt due to the accidents which have just been mentioned, and such accidents do appear to be of the order of two or three centimetres. But in spite of this there can be little doubt that Valentin is justified in drawing the long line passing through the 'mean' of these points, and inferring from them that the mean annual sea level is tending to fall at Aberdeen, to rise at Dunbar, and to rise more sharply at Newlyn. Some of the mean variations found by Valentin are as follows:

*Emergence +, Submergence −[1]

Aberdeen	1897/1912	−2·8 mm. per year		
Dundee	1897/1912	+0·1	,,	,,	,,
Dunbar	1938/1950	−4·7	,,	,,	,,
Newlyn	1938/1951	−5·2	,,	,,	,,

These rates are by no means negligible; indeed the significance of them is apparent when it is realized that since 1938 the level at Newlyn in Cornwall has been falling relative to M.S.L. at the rate of one inch in five years. Such a rate of movement may if it is sustained be a most important factor in a proper understanding of coastal behaviour. The importance of changes in water level to the development of coral features will be remembered in this connection.

Some examples of raised beaches have already been mentioned; but perhaps some of the most remarkable are beaches or strandlines in Norway due to a recent negative movement which are now 600 or more feet above the present sea level; raised beaches have also been found in the West Coast of Scotland, South Wales, Devonshire and Cornwall and the South of Ireland. These features are dealt with at length in geological and geomorphological textbooks.

Proof of submergence is not so clear for the very reason

---

[1] Valentin made a statistical analysis which, for obvious reasons, I have simplified above.

that the water obscures the evidence, but the submergence of huts in Greenland, the submerged forests on many beaches, and the existence of the drowned city of Ys in Brittany are simple evidence of the rising of the water level relative to the land.

These movements must have an important effect upon the coastline for a rising or emergent coast tends to have a smooth outline while the submerged or drowned coast is by comparison irregular and indented.

The reason is not far to seek. On land the erosive forces of streams[1] and glaciers tend to produce irregular and complex contours; by contrast, the erosive action of the sea is more likely to produce a plane surface; an inclined plane it is true, near the coastline, but a surface of which the high places will be steadily worn down, and the hollow places filled up.

That this is so can be demonstrated by examining almost any land map along with a marine chart, on a suitable scale, of the neighbouring sea bed. It will be seen that almost invariably the relief of the latter is more regular than that of the adjoining land. Indeed, the point can be clearly demonstrated in nature by the simple observation of the land surface as compared with the sea bed when exposed at low tide. It is therefore clear that a rise in sea level would almost certainly result in a very indented coastline, at first rocky if not cliffed; while emergence, arising from a lowering of sea level, would produce a smooth coastline, probably of sand.

Probably the most important effect of eustatic and isostatic movements, however, is the part that they play in the formation of many coastal features, notably the barrier islands, and bars like those which lie between the *étangs* and the sea in the South of France. It does not seem possible that the actions of wave and current which

[1] A 'mature' state in the cycle of erosion would provide an exception to this generalization.

we are able to observe now, could, without the intervention of some other process or factor, form such
features. Our enquiry therefore leads us to seek a solution
in the uncertain vertical movements of the kind that we
have been discussing.

Unfortunately our information about these movements
is meagre; doubtless there have been many fluctuations—
it would be interesting to know how many could have
taken place during the formation of coastlines—and
even more, the rates of the various oscillations. At present
it seems doubtful that these problems will ever be solved.

Local Flexure of the Coastal Profile

Bourcart has observed that there are sometimes local
changes in the slopes of strata near the coast, which
appear to be associated with or confined to the coastal
fringe. He describes this bending as a 'flexure', and
attributes it to the deposition of material in the sea to an
extent which depresses the formation under the increased
load, and so causes local bending of the underlying strata.
The process is in fact a minor isostatic adjustment.

From this brief summary of geological considerations
it will be seen that it is not possible to understand coastal
forms or coastal changes without examining all the
geological evidence available. The nature of the material,
whether hard rock or soft, or whether shingle, sand or
mud, will dictate in advance to a large extent what the
marine forces can or cannot do. Many coastal forms are
explained quite simply because they are known to be
emergent or submergent. The account given is very brief
and describes only the kind of geological evidence that
should be looked for. In particular cases the geological
authorities should always be consulted.

CHAPTER III

PROCESSES OF EROSION, TRANSPORT AND DEPOSITION

THE agencies which are capable of moving material on the sea bed are: waves, currents, including tidal streams, and gravity.

In addition to these wind must be considered a very important indirect agent; it transports sand *above* the sea bed, and it is of course the generating force of waves. We shall consider how these forces operate in some detail. It is necessary to examine them individually if we are to understand them fully, but it must be remembered that at any given time and place all four of them are likely to be playing their parts. It is common knowledge that waves stir bed material into suspension, and that in certain circumstances they can transport objects, for instance, a surf bather. It is equally well known that currents are capable of transporting material horizontally; the action of winds is less apparent, but when we consider that they are entirely responsible for the generation of waves, and largely responsible for the formation of ocean currents, it will be seen that they are of the greatest importance. It is gravity which tends to cause material which is in suspension to re-settle; gravity, too, might cause material to roll down a steep slope. Such slopes are rare under the sea, and it is doubtful whether this rolling process is important except on very steep shingle ridges. Little more will be said about the action of gravity, but the behaviour and effects of waves, currents and wind must be examined in some detail. The implications of tides will be introduced into this chapter for two reasons; first because, as the sea rises and falls as the result of tidal behaviour, different levels of beaches become subject to the action of the sea, and secondly because[1] tidal streams are often important factors in the coastwise transport of material.

WAVES

The action of waves is of supreme importance in any study of coastal behaviour, and it is not possible adequately to explain the movement of materials on beaches unless at least the elements of wave behaviour are understood. In what follows a modicum of mathematics is introduced in order to give some idea of the quantities involved, that is to say the velocities and forces which may occur. It is not possible that these few pages can be a complete treatment of wave behaviour; for a subject so large—and so complex—the special publications, to which reference is made, must be consulted.

If we watch large puddles on a gusty day we shall probably see a pattern of ripples or small waves on their surfaces, and careful observation will reveal in miniature much that is important in a study of wave behaviour in the sea. First, it will appear that the stronger the wind blows the larger will the waves be; secondly, if one of two puddles which are otherwise identical is deeper than the other, the waves will be larger in the deeper puddle. It will also be seen that there are no waves on the windward edge of a puddle, but soon tiny wavelets appear moving away from it and the further they go in the

[1] In accordance with naval usage of the terms, the word 'current' is used to indicate the horizontal movement of water due to the earth's rotation and the steady, or trade winds. 'Tidal streams', which at a given time may appear similar, are due to tidal action; the important difference is that the latter are often, indeed usually reversible; the former are not.

direction of the wind the larger they will be until they reach the shallowing water, or the 'beach' on the opposite side where they are gradually retarded; and the fact that their velocities are retarded inevitably mean that the wave length is shortened. Ultimately they are destroyed as with tiny 'plops' they collapse at the edge of the puddle.

This process of wave generation and destruction takes place in the great oceans of the world with the obvious difference that while we can assume that the wind blows uniformly over the whole area of a puddle, there are very complex wind patterns blowing over the enormous expanse of a large ocean, and the directions and velocities of the wind will vary considerably from place to place. Thus, several winds may produce several wave trains, and these in time may combine to form what unhappy seafarers sometimes call a 'confused' sea.

Water surface waves can of course be formed by other means; for instance, if a pebble is dropped into a pool, rings of ripples will move outwards from the point where it entered the water. A ship as it is driven through the water leaves a pattern of waves sometimes known as its 'wash'; and some of the largest waves experienced have been caused by earthquakes or volcanic explosions. The eruption of the volcano of Krakatoa in 1883 produced waves 100 feet high and which affected tide gauges up to a distance of 5,000 miles.

By whatever means they are formed, waves have energy. When the wind blows on the surface of the sea it imparts energy to it, and this energy survives in the form of the waves; when a pebble is dropped on the surface of the water its velocity is reduced so that it loses kinetic energy; this energy is transferred to the water surface in the form of waves. When a ship travels, urged on by engines developing perhaps 100,000 h.p., the only manifestation of that energy left in the sea is the waves on the surface of the water. And if waves in the sea possess energy imparted to the water surface by the wind, it is also true that the waves themselves can impart energy; indeed nearly all the damage done round our coasts, whether to sea walls, cliffs, beaches, or even to wrecked and stranded ships, is the result of battering by waves of enormous energy.

It cannot be too clearly stated that at any given time there are likely to be several, if not many wave trains in the sea, though there are often occasions when one single train stands out very clearly. But for a time we must consider a single wave train; when that is clearly understood it is not difficult to think of a number of trains superimposed upon one another. Nor will any attempt be made here to go into the more abstruse aspects of wave generation, though the matter is dealt with briefly in Chapter IV and Appendices C and D. It is necessary, however, to have some knowledge of the properties of waves if we are to understand their effect on beaches.

We shall assume that a single uniform system of waves has been generated by the action of the wind, and that the waves are trochoidal[1] in form.

In Fig. III.1 the waves are travelling from left to right. The length of wave λ, is the horizontal distance between crests. Wave height, h, is described as the vertical distance from trough to crest; the still water level AA' is the plane surface that the water would assume if all wave action was stopped. Note that it will *not* be midway between trough and crest if the wave form is trochoidal, but it will be midway if the form is sinusoidal. The wave *period, t*, is the interval of time between the passage of crests past a given point; this can be observed roughly with a stop-watch by timing the crests past, for instance, an upright of a pier. In the Mediterranean it is very common to find a wave period of about 6 seconds; wave periods of

[1] It is sometimes assumed that waves have a sinusoidal form.

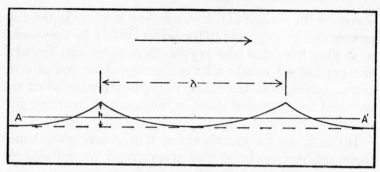

Fig. III.1.—Trochoidal Waves.

20 seconds have been measured in the Atlantic. If we can measure wave lengths, and their periods, it is easy to determine their speeds c, for obviously:

$$\lambda = ct \qquad . \qquad . \qquad . \qquad . \qquad (1)$$

The steepness of waves is represented by h/λ; that is, the ratio of the height to the length from crest to crest. This factor can vary widely; for instance what is known as a swell might be composed of waves whose height is of the order of 2 feet, but whose length is 1,000 feet; in this case the steepness factor would be 1 in 500. At the other end of the scale there is a definite upper limit of steepness of $1/7$; such waves have a crest angle of 120°. Any process (for example, generating winds or a shelving beach) which increases the steepness factor, or in consequence decreases the crest angle, can go no further than $1/7$ for the one or 120° for the other, for at this stage the wave becomes unstable and collapses and 'white horses' or 'breakers' will occur. Very steep waves are found during storms when they are being generated. As might well be seen in the puddle referred to above, the longer the wind acts upon the waves, and the stronger that wind is, the more the waves will tend to increase in height and length; and the longer the waves become the faster they will move.

44

PLATE I

Crown copyright, reproduced by permission of H.M.S.O.

Crown copyright, reproduced by permission of H.M.S.O.

Upper: Elegug Stacks, Pembrokeshire, in Carboniferous Limestone
Lower: Sea stack and natural arch in schists. West Burra, Shetland

PLATE II

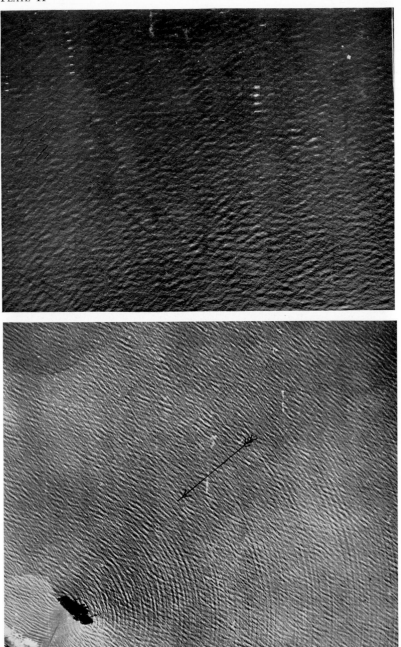

Upper: Short-crested waves in deep water

Lower: Short-crested waves travelling in the direction of the arrow reflected—in a concentric series—by a wrecked ship

In deep water the velocity of waves, c, is given by:

$$c = \sqrt{\frac{g\lambda}{2\pi}} \qquad . \qquad . \qquad . \qquad (2)$$

from which it is clear that there is a relationship between the length of waves and their velocities. But if the wind blows long enough the waves will move with a velocity equal to that of the wind itself. This is a general and reasonable assumption about which there is some dis-agreement among so-called authorities; the truth is that records of wind and wave velocities are so inexact that the general statement does not admit of absolute proof.

The distance from the observer to the nearest wind-ward shore is known as the 'fetch' in that direction. The 'fetch'[1] of beaches on the West Coast of France is 2,000 miles, that is to say the distance to the American con-tinent; at Dover it is about 20 miles in a S.E. direction. Thus large waves are likely to reach a coastline if the greatest fetch is in the direction of the prevailing wind, always supposing that the velocities of the prevailing winds are great. This is why large waves are found on the Cornish coast; they are not so great in the North Sea unless the wind is from the North, or a little West of North—in which direction the fetch is great. Similarly in the Straits of Dover a S.E. wind will not produce very large waves, while winds from the S.W. will.

Once a wave train has been generated in the open sea it will proceed in a direction normal to the wave crests with a velocity determined by the wave lengths (see equation 2), unless it is subsequently affected by winds from a direction different from the first. Should the wind drop the waves will gradually decay. That is, their heights will gradually decrease; there is some evidence that the wave lengths and therefore velocities increase slightly at the same time, though this change is

---

[1] 'Fetch' is referred to again on pp. 91 and 209.

hardly of practical importance to us. It is these decayed waves, with a small height to length ratio, which are called 'swell'.

Wave sizes should be discussed with caution, since in the open sea when they are at their greatest it is very difficult to make reliable measurements, and their very grandeur, which is often frightening, tends to distort the observer's judgment. The opinion of the casual observer is very unreliable; for instance, on a transatlantic passage on the *Queen Mary* the writer once asked a number of passengers to estimate the height of the waves when his

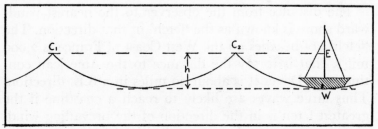

Fig. III.2.—Method of assessing wave heights at sea.

own opinion was that they were from 8 to 10 feet high; the estimates of the passengers asked varied from 15 to 40 feet. But it is possible to be more precise than this, and two methods of measurement are worth mentioning; the first to measure the wave *period* in seconds with a stopwatch, which (see Appendix B) gives the length very simply, while for estimates of height, if the observer climbs into the rigging of a ship to a point E from which he sees consecutive wave crests C_1 C_2 in line, then the wave height will clearly be EW, where W is the waterline of the ship.

Vaughan Cornish, who was an enthusiastic and careful observer of waves, has placed on record some interesting observations of wave sizes. He records seeing at Branksome Chine near Bournemouth a group of breakers whose average period was 19 seconds, and this he computed to correspond with a deep water speed of 66·5 miles per hour. They continued to arrive for 44 minutes. It seems certain that they were generated at the height of an Atlantic storm, and, being larger and swifter than those generated after, as well as before, this peak, outstripped them in their progress towards our coast. It is probable, though Cornish does not record the fact, that the smaller waves arrived later, not so much in their order of generation *chronologically* as in order of size, and therefore speed. Cornish writes: 'The greatest wave period which I have ever recorded was on February 1st 1899, at Branksome Chine when a group of twelve large breakers came at intervals of 22·5 seconds, corresponding to a speed of 78·75 miles per hour, the whole group occupying rather more than 4 minutes in arrival, a normal duration for a squall.' Cornish was interested in the relation between the gust speeds during storms and the average, or steady wind velocity, as well as in the ratio of wind velocity to the speed of the waves generated. In this connection he writes: 'During the storm of December 6th, 1929, the anemometer (readings) taken at Scilly recorded a momentary velocity of 111 miles per hour, the greatest ever recorded in the British Isles. The maximum sustained velocity in this gale was 68 miles per hour. Waves travelling with eight-tenths of the speed of the strongest momentary gust, that is to say, at 89 miles per hour, would have a period of 25·4 seconds, which is much beyond that of any breakers which I have observed.'

Of wave heights, Cornish records 41 feet in mid-Atlantic, when they were 'remarkably regular billows'. A Captain Cheret reported waves 45 feet high between Southampton and the Azores during a storm when the winds were of Force 9. The officers of the ship thought that these were the largest waves that they had experienced.

Even larger waves have been recorded, though their assessment has been based on less convincing evidence than those quoted above. Yet there is reason to believe that the estimate of a height of 70 feet for waves on the route from Yokohama to Puget Sound is not far from the truth, while a report from the S.S. *Majestic* in 1923 suggested heights between 60 and 90 feet. A report from the Atlantic in recent years mentioned a single wave 100 feet high. All of the estimates quoted above were made, not from wild guesses, but from deliberate assessments by the officers of the ships; but the difficulties are great, and many accounts of wave height should be treated with caution.

ENERGY OF WAVES

The property of waves which concerns us most closely is their capacity to do work, or their energy, and it is important to have some idea of the magnitude of the forces which are at work when waves are attacking any coastal feature.

There are times when the waves are almost entirely ineffective; when they are so feeble that they constitute a negligible force. For instance the sea is sometimes so calm that there is no sand in suspension; when sand grains on the sea bed are undisturbed, and only a fragment of a dead leaf, or some equally light, small body, is seen to move on the sea bed. It is reasonable to assume in such circumstances that neither erosion nor deposition is taking place.

But a rough sea presents a very different picture. During storms wrecked ships weighing hundreds of tons may be lifted and bumped along the sea bed; piers may be broken, and not infrequently steel girders forming the upper structure of ships are bent. At such times there would be a large amount of sand in suspension on the beach and even rocks might be lifted clear of the bottom. Then the bed material would be moved horizontally by the waves themselves, and at the same time it would be carried along by the prevailing currents.

The energy of large waves can be enormous; it is difficult to talk in precise terms of the energy in a given wave system because it is difficult to harness the energy, or to apply any system of measurement to waves, but Lamb gives a formula which gives a theoretical value.

For energy per unit length of front:

$$EG = \frac{\frac{1}{4}\rho g a^2 \sigma}{\kappa} \left(1 + \frac{2\kappa h}{\sinh -\kappa h}\right)$$

or $\frac{1}{2}g\rho a^2 \times$ the group velocity . . . (3)

Where a = wave amplitude = $\frac{1}{2}$ wave height.

λ = wave length ($\kappa = \dfrac{2\pi}{\lambda}$ = wave number)

t = wave period ($\sigma = \dfrac{2\pi}{t}$ = frequence)

h = mean depth of water

ρ = density

g = gravity.

We will substitute in this formula the data for two wave conditions, first on a calm day, with a gentle wave that would be noticed probably only as it turns over at the water's edge; the second case for really large Atlantic rollers which might fling themselves against the Cornish cliffs, or against the West Coast of Ireland. Let us assume for the first wave a period of three seconds, and a height of one foot; the energy per foot of coastline would be about 0·4 horsepower. For the great storm waves, of period 14 seconds and height 20 feet (the deep water length of such a wave would be about 1,000 feet), the energy would be of the order of 77 horsepower per foot of coastline. Such are the forces that have to be reckoned with by engineers who design groynes and sea walls; it is not surprising therefore that they are sometimes breached or that sea coasts without artificial defences are damaged by the attack of the sea.

This figure of nearly 100 horsepower per foot length of coastline is an indication of how fast beach or cliff material can be moved; and we shall see that it may be transported in almost any direction. If we imagine a steam hammer of this kind hammering the cliffs or the sea wall, or comparable machinery throwing sand or shingle into suspension so that it can be transported by the action of currents, we have some idea of what our coastlines have to suffer.

On the other hand, it is not true to say that there is a close relation between the energy of waves and the damage that they do; granite cliffs, for instance, have enormous resistance, and so have some structures, either due to the strength of the materials of which they are made, or to the skill with which they have been designed. The energy of the waves is there, however, and if the waves have been halted the energy has been dissipated somehow; the capacity of the coastline to withstand wave action depends upon geological considerations which have been discussed in Chapter II.

There have been some notable instances of the destructive power of waves, one of the most remarkable being at Wick, in Scotland, where a mass of masonry, part of the breakwater, was moved by waves during a severe storm. In 1898, part of Peterhead breakwater, a piece of masonry weighing 3,300 tons, was shifted two inches, and it has been estimated that the blow which did this would be equal to two tons per square foot. In 1894 a monolithic mass weighing 1,700 tons was carried 105 feet into the harbour during a severe gale. These instances show at once the force of the waves, and the necessity for suitable design and sound construction when building sea defences.

Lighthouse engineers because of the particular circumstances in which they work are fully aware of the forces which their structures must withstand. It is recorded that during the erection of the tower at Dhu Heartach southwest of Mull, fourteen joggled stones, each of two tons weight, were washed away after having been set in cement at a height of 37 feet above high water. Soon after the completion of the Bishop Rock Lighthouse in 1858, the five hundredweight fog bell, fixed to the lantern gallery 100 feet above high water mark, was washed away during storms. There have been many records of waves and debris being thrown over lighthouses more than 100 feet above high water level. These examples of the movement of heavy structures at sea level, and of large objects at comparatively great heights are startling examples of the capacity of waves to do work whether it be destructive or constructive. Storms of such severity as those referred to above are of rare occurrence, but time is long, and in geological time it is reasonable to assume that any length of coastline exposed to a fetch of 300 miles or more, has suffered many extremely damaging storms.

It has already been said that more than one wave train can exist in a given area of the sea at the same time; this must be so for, over a large ocean, the wind directions and velocities vary widely. For instance, a wave train generated by westerly winds in mid-Atlantic might travel eastwards to find northerly winds off the West Coast of Ireland, and this northerly wind would develop a system of south-going waves which would be superimposed upon the first system.

Often it is possible to see three distinct wave systems of different lengths and travelling in different directions. Plate II is a photograph showing two wave systems. The first is travelling in the direction of the arrow; but some of them encounter the wreck of a ship and are clearly reflected as a concentric system radiating from it. When two intersecting systems of nearly the same length occur the result is the 'short crested' wave. This phenomenon is by no means uncommon. In deep water the surface of the water appears to be a rather confused pattern of pyramids of water instead of a series of long lines of waves. Fig. III.3 shows how such a pattern can result from two wave systems; one of these systems is shown in

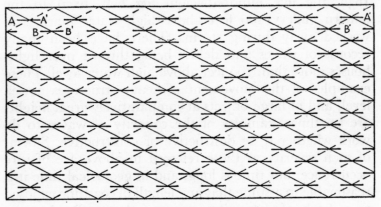

FIG. III.3.—The formation of short crested waves.

dashes and the other in firm lines. When these two systems combine the result is a series of heaps of water such as AA' and BB'. It will be readily realized that an increased number of systems will cause a very confused sea; the kind of sea that can be extremely uncomfortable to those who sail in small boats. An air photograph of short crested waves will be found on Plate II.

The short crested wave pattern will not be apparent to the observer on shore. The reason is simple; wave refraction, which is dealt with later in this chapter, will cause all the constituent wave systems to assume an alignment parallel to the water's edge; thus, instead of the deep water criss-cross pattern we shall see an irregular sequence of waves, probably of different sizes, approaching the coastline parallel to one another.

It has been shown by Dr. Deacon of the National Institute of Oceanography that at any given time a large number of different wave trains may be running. His observations are made with a wave detector which is a kind of inverted[1] echo sounder. This produces a profile which is made up of all the wave systems which arrive at the selected point of observation. With an ingenious instrument for analysing them he has been able to ascertain the periods of all the constituent systems.

We must now consider what happens to the waves, which we have supposed to be generated in deep water, when they approach the coast which they beset. Inevitably they are stopped by the coast; either suddenly by cliffs arising out of deep water, or gradually by the shelving bottom of a sandy beach. Probably every reader of this book has been fascinated to see great rollers approach a beach, to see them gradually slowed down until they break; but after breaking they continue to move more slowly until they stop at the water's edge. Plate V is an excellent illustration of this process.

The rate of retardation can be expressed mathematically; a useful expression for wave velocity is:

$$c^2 = \frac{g\lambda}{2\pi} \tanh \frac{2d\pi}{\lambda} \qquad . \qquad . \qquad . \quad (4)$$

in which λ represents the wave length and d the water depth. There is a more accurate, but much more cumbersome expression for wave velocity in terms of wave length and water depth which introduces the height, or amplitude of the waves, but equation (4) is accurate enough for all ordinary purposes.

[1] For a description of the echo sounder see p. 170.

Equation (4) is expressed graphically in Appendix A.[1] The curves are drawn for wave lengths 10, 20, 30, 50, 100, 200 and 1,000 feet and we can see, for any of these waves, what their velocities will be in waters of varying depths. For instance, a wave 50 feet long in deep water travels at a velocity of 16 feet per second until it encounters a depth of 21 feet. Then it gradually slows down; in 11 feet of water it is travelling at 15 feet per second; in water 5 feet deep at a little under 12 feet per second. Larger waves begin to slow down in greater depths as can be seen from the diagram. Naturally, since the velocities and lengths of the waves are reduced as the waves advance up a beach their energy too is gradually diminished. This very important fact must not be forgotten; it means that where waves attack the foot of cliffs which are in deep water, the whole energy of the waves is hurled at the cliffs; on a flat sandy beach the energy is dissipated over a very wide belt; on shingle beaches, the width of the breaker zone is much narrower, so that the attack of the same wave system on a shingle beach, which is relatively steep and narrow, is more localized and therefore more powerful than on a beach of sand.

When the generating forces no longer act upon waves they continue to progress at approximately the same speed, but the height falls off gradually as the waves decay. If they travel far enough the height/length ratio gradually falls off until the pattern becomes what is known as 'swell'. As the waves approach a shelving beach the height gradually increases to a maximum at the plunge point, and having broken, the height of the subsequent surf waves falls off to zero at the water's edge.

Where swell approaches shoal water so that the waves

[1] Lack of space precludes a full treatment of 'group velocity'. Briefly, there may be wave trains—for example, those radiating from a pebble dropped in water—which, *as a group*, move at half the speed of c in equation (4). Wave *energy* is transmitted at the group velocity of the waves.

'feel bottom' and are retarded, the wave height is increased at the same time although, because of the very small height/length ratio, they are unlikely to approach the conditions for breaking. The increase in height gives rise to what is known as 'ground swell'.

Particle Motion in Wave action

In deep water, which is generally understood to be water deeper than the wave length, the particles of water

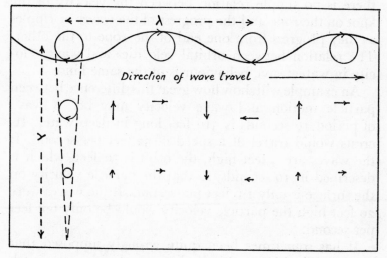

Direction of wave travel

FIG. III.4.—Orbital motion of waves in deep water.

move in orbits whose diameters are equal to the amplitude or heights of the waves, and with a period equal to the wave period; but the orbits decrease in diameter with increasing depth as indicated in Fig. III.4, there being no motion[1] when $d = \lambda$; submarines frequently submerge to depths at which wave action is hardly felt. Thus the *particle* velocities on the surface are a function of wave height and period; the *wave* velocity is, however, a

[1] This is an approximation which in shallow water is precise enough for our purposes; it is not strictly true at great depths.

function of wave length or wave period. The relation between particle velocity and wave velocity therefore is not a simple one. An illustration may help to explain this relation.

Imagine that a rope, lying in a straight line on the ground, is held at one end and waved up and down so as to cause ripples, or waves. These waves travel quite quickly from one end to the other but at a fixed point, say a knot, on the rope the movement is quite small; there is no simple relation between the velocity of the knot on the rope and the progress of the waves or ripples as they progress from one end of the rope to the other. The relation between orbital velocities and wave velocity in water wave behaviour is of the same kind.

An example will show how great this difference between particle motion and wave velocity may be. A wave of period 10 seconds is 512 feet long in deep water. Its crests would travel at a speed of 52 feet per second. If the waves are 5 feet high, the orbit is 5π feet, which is described in 10 seconds, so that the particle velocity on the surface is only 1·6 feet per second. If the waves were 20 feet high the particle velocity would be only 6·4 feet per second.

It has sometimes been quite wrongly supposed that particle velocities, and indeed wave velocities, are much greater than they are, by considering the heights to which water, and sometimes stones, are thrown against such structures as lighthouses. Using the usual formulae for the behaviour of particles under gravity it may at first sight appear that the initial velocities of particles projected to such heights are vastly greater than those computed above. This is indeed so; but these initial velocities do not arise from the deep water behaviour of the waves, but from pressures built up in water which is precipitated from the crests of breaking waves into funnel shapes in the rock on which they break and this produces an effect which is in some ways comparable with water forced from the nozzle of a hose.

It is to be understood that the circular orbits described above are characteristic of deep water waves. What happens to such waves when they enter shallower water? This is clearly demonstrated in a glass-sided wave tank in which model experiments can be carried out. Here it will be seen that whereas at A where the depth $= d$, d being $\nless \lambda$ (Fig. III.5) the particle motion is circular, in shoal water at B the circular orbits are distorted by the bottom of the tank, and the particles move in ellipses.

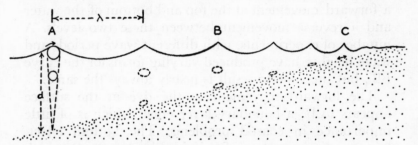

Fig. III.5.—Orbital motion of waves on a beach.

As the water decreases in depth the short axis of the ellipse shortens until, near the water line at C, the motion becomes simply to and fro, or up and down the beach. This can be clearly seen at the water's edge on a fairly calm day; grains of sand or a twig of wood can be seen alternately going up the beach with the waves and receding as the swash of the wave recedes; but it suffers no perceptible vertical motion.

It is relevant at this stage to mention another effect of wave action known as *mass transport*. If in a glass-sided wave tank in which unbroken waves are running, we drop a trace of dye, such as fluorescene, as indicated at AA′ in Fig. III.6, the constituent particles of the trace will move in orbits in a way which has already been

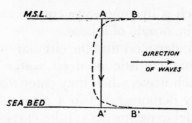

Fig. III.6.—'Mass transport' under wave action in a finite channel.

described, but another effect will soon appear. The vertical streak AA' will assume a form something like that shown by the pecked line BB'. That is to say, there is a forward movement at the top and bottom of the water and a reverse movement between these two levels. A number of experiments, with different wave periods and wave heights, have produced varying forms for the curve BB', but the general result is nearly always the same.

The forward movement of the dye at the surface appears to be a boundary layer effect which is of little importance in coastal problems. The bottom effect, however, is important; for it is this movement which transports the bottom material. It is doubtful whether the change indicated in Fig. III.6 is a very precise indicator of what happens at sea. In a finite wave trough, a forward movement at the surface and at the bottom must be compensated by a movement in a contrary sense somewhere, which doubtless explains the recession of water at the middle levels. It is probable that in a wide sea there is a forward movement at all levels, with the greatest movement on the sea bed. In fact a general movement of the sea known as *mass transport* is known to exist. Quite simply this means that in addition to the oscillatory movement of particles already described there is, under wave action, a tendency for the whole cross section of the water to move—slowly—in the same direction as the wind, or, more precisely, of wave travel.

58

This is an extremely important phenomenon; and since the time has come to deal with the effect of wave behaviour on beaches it should be very clearly borne in mind that, under unbroken waves, particles are[1] moving along the bottom in a to-and-fro motion and at the same time are being gradually pushed shorewards.

This is happening not only to a thin layer of sand or shingle particles on the bed of the sea; it is happening also to such sand or shingle as may be in suspension. If the waves are large, the turbulence will be increased, and there will be more material available for transport whether by wave or current action. Those who swim in the sea will be well aware of how on a calm day there is no sand in suspension and the water is clear; but when the sea is rough one is occasionally struck in the face by a small stone, while the sea may be thick with sand. At such times the rate of transport of material must be enormous.

At last the oscillatory waves reach a position on the beach such that their amplitudes are roughly equal to the still water (or waveless) depth of the water. In their approach to this point the heights of the crests have been increased slightly, and, as has been explained on p. 53, the lengths are shortened as the wave velocities decrease. Thus the height/length ratio increases until the wave becomes unstable and, as we say, 'breaks'.

The breaking of the wave, and the nature of the water movement on the sea bed before and after the break, is fundamental to an understanding of beach behaviour because the characters and actions of waves before and after the break are very different. In Fig. III.7 the point P where the wave breaks is called the 'Plunge point', and along the whole coast there is a 'Plunge line', which

---

[1] This statement is valid when the only factor to be taken into account is wave action. As will be seen elsewhere the effect can be overwhelmed by other agencies such as an offshore wind.

is the first line of breakers. After the plunge point the wave height becomes gradually less until it disappears completely at the water's edge. After the plunge point the oscillatory motion of the wave ceases; as the wave collapses a whole mass of water is precipitated downwards and forwards, and it proceeds bodily towards the water's edge. Surf bathers will realize quite clearly the difference between the wave action between S and P

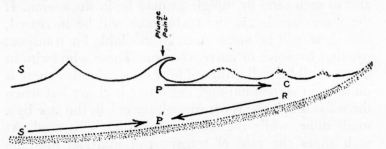

FIG. III.7.—The constructive and destructive action of waves.

(Fig. III.7) and between P and C. It is not possible to ride a surf board between S and P, but between P and C[1] if the bather can mount his board he will be carried along at the speed of the wave. Those who have not ridden surf boards may demonstrate the difference in wave action in another way; throw a floating object into the sea seaward of P, and it rises and falls, with little horizontal movement; in fact it is almost true to say that it remains in the same place in the sea; but if the same object be thrown into the surf landward of P it will quickly be carried on the surface to the waterline. The band of drift material along the water edge or the 'drift line' is further evidence of this particular action of the sea. It is most unusual to find any heavy objects among the 'floatable' drift on a sand beach, which is one reason

[1] For obvious reasons Fig. III.7 is very foreshortened. There would often be six or seven surf waves between P and C.

PLATE III

Upper: Erosion at the back of a sand beach during storm. Sidi Ferruch, Algeria

Lower: Runnel and bar formation.   Near Morib, West Coast of Malaya

PLATE IV

Upper: Parallel offshore bars. West Coast of Italy.
Lower: Crescentic bars, double series. Anse de Pampelonne, Mediterranean France

for supposing that the motion along the sea bed land-ward of the plunge line is not the same as that on the surface. There is another observation which swimmers can make for themselves. To swim on the surface from C to P against the surf waves is difficult, but it is relatively easy to swim along the bottom, where what is sometimes called the 'undertow' helps to carry one to seaward at a pace which is sometimes quite remarkable. It can also be observed that it is easy—if one can breathe—to swim with the surf waves; but to stand in water five feet deep in a surf zone is difficult because the foaming waves tend to carry the top half of one's body landward, while the undertow is sweeping one's feet away in the opposite direction; hence the panic of non-swimmers. The pheno-menon is clearly seen in a wave tank where evidence of the return current RP′ is unmistakable.

Such observations as the writer has made in wave tanks have been on too small a scale to indicate the exact nature of this seaward trend under surf waves. It might be, and almost certainly is, an excess of the seaward part of an oscillatory motion over the landward part; it is almost certainly never a steady current, and there is evidence that it is stronger under the troughs than under the crests. While a detailed knowledge of its behaviour would be interesting, the really important fact is that it exists at all. A few examples will show how important it is to take into account this return trend.

Let us study Fig. III.7 again, ignoring the movement of the water on the surface, and concerning ourselves only with the water movement on the sea bed where the material is ready to be rolled, or is raised into suspension by the turbulence of the water under wave action.[1]

From S′ to P′ the material is pushed shoreward, more

[1] As has already been explained the point P moves from time to time in accordance with the wave amplitude; waves in general break when the still water depth is equal to the wave amplitude in deep water.

rapidly in the shallow water than the deep, because the wave energy applied to the sea bed decreases as the water depth increases. This action may be seen in the sea on almost any calm day. From R to P', on the other hand, the material is pushed to seaward. This action is not so easy to *see*, though it may often be felt, as has been explained above. This return action is more powerful than the action S'P, because the water is shallower, and the wave energy applied to the sea bed is greater.

It would appear that if Fig. III.7 fairly represents the state of affairs on a beach, there ought to be an accumulation of sand at P', and it may have occurred to the reader that he is not aware of having seen such banks. The truth is that unless some other disturbing factor exists these accumulations do in fact exist; indeed the offshore bar, so common in the Mediterranean, see p. 110, is caused quite simply by the concerted action of these two trends. That the bar exists in the Mediterranean and not round our own coasts is due entirely to the circumstances that the Mediterranean is almost tideless. In Fig. III.7 there will be an accumulation at P' if the wave action goes on long enough for S'P' and RP' to carry appreciable loads. It is apparent that this is unlikely to happen on a tidal beach. Even assuming that the wave height remains constant, on a beach where the tidal range is 20 feet and the gradient 1 in 100, P' moves over a horizontal distance of 2,000 feet or so in about six hours, so that there is no time for any accumulation to occur. Besides this the horizontal position of P' can change rapidly due to changes in the wave amplitude. Wave amplitudes can change very rapidly: for instance, when surveying a beach in Algeria the author's section arrived on an afternoon when the weather was fair and there was hardly a ripple on the water; by the time they had changed and carried the boat, a dory, from the back of the beach, it was impossible to launch it because waves from three to four feet high were running. On the beach in question the resultant horizontal movement of the plunge point was about eighty yards.

The offshore bar is dealt with in some detail on pp. 110 et seq, but in the Mediterranean there are few exceptions to the general rule that there is at least one such bar, and this is situated on the plunge line of the greatest waves that arrive on the beach.

Yet one more example to prove the existence of the return trend RP′ should be mentioned here. It is generally assumed that storm waves are 'destructive'; that is to say, they remove material from the beach, and that during calmer weather the wave action is 'constructive', which means that material is replaced on the beach. There have been many attempts to define exactly what constitutes the destructive and constructive characters of waves; most writers are agreed that the constructive action is due to a swell; or to waves whose height/length ratio is small; attempts to classify the destructive waves are more diverse, though it is generally agreed that they are fiercer than constructive waves and that they occur during storms when the height/length ratio of the waves is greater. There is a wealth of evidence to show that, until careful quantitative observations provide a better definition, unbroken waves, whose motion is oscillatory, are constructive, and broken or surf waves are destructive; that this is so of sand beaches is demonstrated by their profiles under the two kinds of wave action. In Fig. III.8 suppose a profile after a long spell of calm seas to be CC_1; suppose further that a storm occurs with waves such that there is a plunge point at or near P; material will then be moved so as to form a profile as indicated in the pecked line, the material being deposited under or near P. The higher levels of this storm or winter beach will be denuded, and there may be a sharp nick at the back of the beach. (See Plate III.)

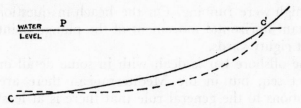

FIG. III.8.—'Summer' and 'Winter' beach profiles.

The effects described above refer specifically to beaches of sand; in principle the wave movement should be just the same on shingle, but the very nature of shingle beaches brings about certain differences. The gradients of sand beaches vary very widely, but gradients of 1 in 30 to 1 in 100 are common. Shingle beaches are much steeper, and gradients of 1 in 3 to 1 in 10 are often found while some ridges are as steep as 1 in 1. On such gradients there may be no surf, and no breakers, conditions may be such that the break occurs as one crash of descending water on the steep face of the shingle slope; it is very difficult to observe in detail what happens, the sequence of events is even more difficult to reconstruct, especially since it is quite impossible to make reliable observations on shingle beaches during storms because of the violence of the sea. The following description indicates some of the effects of storm waves on a shingle ridge; I make no attempt to weave the parts of the story into a whole; it would be imprudent to do so because slow motion photography of the action in a large scale tank is capable of demonstrating clearly and unmistakably what does take place.

In Fig. III.9 tidal rise and fall is neglected, though it should be remembered that at the level of low springs there is often little shingle; usually it exists as a belt above this level.

As the waves approach the shore they are, up to the point P', constructive; the shingle movement there is

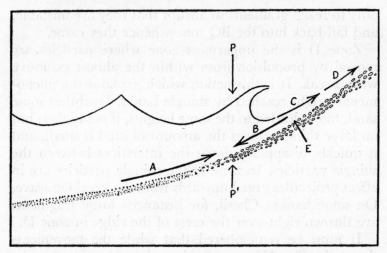

FIG. III.9.—The effect of wave action on a shingle beach.

indicated by the arrow A. Under the breaker is a very strong destructive action which is indicated by arrow B; the top of this combing-down belt often overlaps a higher belt C where the waves which here are running up the beach face as a sheet of water transport the shingle fragments shoreward. There is thus a narrow zone E where the oscillatory movement of the particles which exists everywhere is nearly balanced. The action in zone C is very complex, and is not yet clearly understood. It is hereabouts that the characteristic shingle ridges are formed. At the upper limit of zone C there must be a strong tendency towards an upward and shoreward movement of material, since there is more shingle-bearing water going in this direction than in the opposite direction. If arrow C represents a volume V of water with shingle in suspension which is hurled upwards, a large proportion of the water returns to M.S.L. by percolation through the shingle of the bank and so can carry no shingle with it. It is probable that the rate of building in this zone is so great that steep ridges are built only to reach gradients so abrupt that they are unstable, and fall back into the BC zone whence they came.

Zone D is the uppermost zone where particles are moved by propulsion from within the almost explosive wave break. It is this action which explains the phenomenal height reached by shingle banks. Doubtless some sand, too, is hurled to the same heights, if not higher, but on large shingle ridges the amount of sand is small, and it quickly disappears down the interstices between the shingle particles. In zone D the shingle particles are in effect projectiles urged upwards from the breaking wave. On some banks—Chesil, for instance—large fragments are thrown right over the crest of the ridge in zone D.

It must be remembered that while the movements shown in Fig. III.9 are taking place the tide may be rising or falling, and so adding further to the complications of the process.

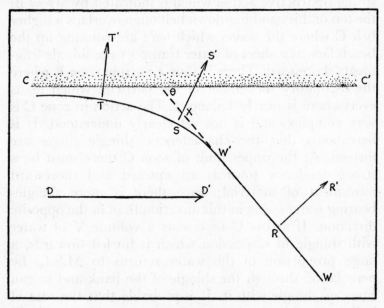

Fig. III.10.—Refraction of waves.

66

WAVE REFRACTION AND OBLIQUE WAVES

For obvious reasons there must be many occasions on which waves do not travel in such a direction that their crests are parallel with the coast. In Fig. III.10 waves travelling in a direction RR' have fronts WW' making an angle θ with the coast CC'. Such waves are called *oblique* waves, and as they proceed inshore they become *refracted* or bent. It has been explained on p. 53 that waves travel more slowly as the water depths decrease. Thus, in Fig. III.10 the wave WT is retarded by an amount XS at S; at T, where the water is even more shallow, the wave velocity is less and thus retardation greater, so that the wave front is curved as is shown by the line RST; thus the directions of travel at the various points are RR', SS' and TT'. On flat beaches it is sometimes observed that where the deep water waves are oblique the waves inshore are very nearly parallel to the coastline.[1]

The effect of such waves on bottom material is simply understood if we apply what we know about the constructive and destructive waves to the direction in which the waves are travelling. Clearly in addition to the usual effects normal to the coastline, there will be coastwise movements. Seaward of the plunge line there will be a coastwise drift in the direction DD' due to the component of the bottom thrust in this direction as well as to the component of mass transport. Usually, inside the plunge line the obliquity of the waves will have been so reduced that the longshore component is small; but there

---

[1] If the crests of unrefracted waves of velocity V_0 make an angle θ_0 with a straight coastline, the angle of refraction θ at a shallower depth is given by

$$\sin \theta = \frac{V \sin \theta_0}{V_0}$$

where V is the velocity of the waves at the point in shallow water. Appendices A and B may be used for determining this velocity.

may well be cases when the obliquity is sufficient to cause movement in the direction opposite to DD′ in this zone. Such a state of affairs must be rare. Suppose that in Fig. III.10 the plunge point of the waves were at S. There would be a bottom movement in the direction XS, and this would give a coastwise component in the direction D′D; but the component would be small, and it is doubtful whether the reversal of direction due to this cause is ever important.

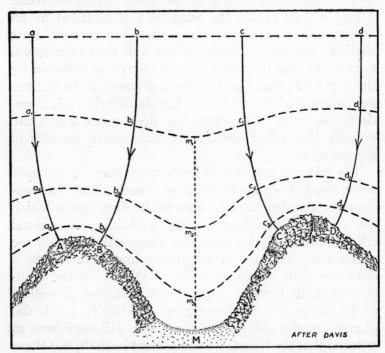

Fig. III.11.—Distribution of wave energy on an indented coastline.

Davis has drawn attention to the fact that refraction causes wave energy to be concentrated on the headlands of an indented coast, and to be reduced in the bays where the beaches are likely to be situated. It is doubtful whether the matter is of great importance in an attempt to explain the changes that take place on a coastline, but it is certainly true that the fiercest wave action occurs on the promontories.

Fig. III.11, which is a variation of Davis' diagram, shows waves $a\ b\ c\ d$ and $a_1\ b_1\ c_1\ d_1$ advancing towards the coastline A B C D. Due to refraction they will ultimately assume the form $a_2\ b_2\ c_2\ d_2$ and $a_3\ b_3\ c_3\ d_3$, and the directions will become $a\ a_1\ a_2\ a_3$ A, $b\ b_1\ b_2\ b_3$ B, etc.

Davis points out that the energy of the waves along the distance ab in deep water is concentrated by refraction into the small length of coastline AB, while that of an equal length bc becomes dispersed over a greater length BC. This is undoubtedly true, but the concentration is even greater than this, for while a wave travelling from m dissipates its energy over a distance m_1 M, the wave starting from b_1 has expended all its energy in the shorter distance b_1 B. It seems more reasonable to argue therefore that the energy represented by the area $a\ a_1\ b_1\ b$ becomes concentrated into the area $a_2\ a_3\ b_3\ b_2$, while that of an equal area $b\ b_1\ c_1\ c$ is dispersed over the area represented by $b_2\ b_3\ c_3\ c_2$; a much greater concentration than Davis suggested. It is clear, therefore, that the promontories of a coastline are subject to more violent wave action than the bays; a circumstance which is apparent to any observer who comes to visit two such places during storms.

Dominant and Prevalent Waves

These terms are frequently used by writers on coastal problems. It is doubtful whether they are of any real importance, since wave behaviour admits of precise description in terms of period and height; and in so far as these definitions can be precise and quantitative, any other definition must be *faute de mieux*. But statistics for a given coastal station might show that waves of a given size and shape occur more often than others; if so, these waves could fairly be called *prevalent*; they could, for instance, be associated with a *prevailing* wind, though this association must not be pressed too far, for winds are generally deemed to *prevail* in directions only; not in force. A *dominant* wave is one which *dominates* the coast; which is responsible for the preponderance of the sculpture and transport. That the prevailing waves are not synonymous with the dominant waves can be readily proved by the following example. Let us make the rough, but for this purpose sufficient, approximation that the daily amount of work done by waves is ch^3 where c is a constant, and h the wave amplitude in feet.

Now if on 364 days of the year the prevailing wave height were one foot, the work done would be $364c$. But if on the 365th day, a severe storm arose and that the wave height was 10 feet, the amount of work done in that single day would be $c10^3$, or $1000c$; that is to say, three times as much as the *prevailing* waves had done in the rest of the year. Clearly in a sense the larger waves can be said to *dominate* the beach. The disadvantage of such terms is that in the example quoted the prevailing winds were associated with a gently constructive process, while on the 365th day the waves were destructive, which is a distinction not often made in the textbooks. It is for this reason that, while it is desirable that the terms 'prevalent' and 'dominant' should be understood when read, it is wise not to use them when writing. An excellent example of the confusion which may arise from using the terms is given on p. 111, where it will be seen that dominant waves indeed dominate the outer two bars and demolish the inner, while the prevalent waves produce most feeble results on the inner bar and have no effect on the outer.

Before concluding this section on waves and their action it is necessary to emphasize another extremely important result of wave action to which a passing reference has already been made in pp. 19–20, that is their ability to raise bottom material in suspension. In a study of coastal behaviour we are not concerned with the discussion as to whether sand is disturbed in water depths of 200 feet or whether, as has been reported, stones weighing one pound in weight are washed into lobster pots at a depth of 180 feet off Land's End. Our concern is with depths of three fathoms and less, and in these small depths there is no doubt that the amount of sand and shingle in suspension can be very great. The matter is of some importance. In an article in a reputable scientific journal it is argued that because the longshore current is only about half a knot, no bottom material can be moved because such a small velocity is not powerful enough to pick up even a grain of sand. It is not, of course, necessary for the current to *pick up* the material, and a little thought will convince the reader how fast a steady current of half a knot can move material once the turbulent action of the waves has raised it in suspension; it would of course be quite ineffective without wave action.[1]

TIDES AND TIDAL STREAMS

It is not necessary for the student of coastal morphology to possess a detailed knowledge of the theory of tides; those who are interested in the subject are referred to suitable literature at the end of this book. It is necessary, however, to consider two tidal phenomena which often have a considerable effect on coastal changes. First the effect of the periodic rise and fall of the sea which causes the action of the waves and currents to act at different levels—and by implication in different zones—of the coastline, and secondly the effect of tidal streams.

[1] A rough calculation has shown that during a moderate storm 4 tons of sand were in suspension per 1 yard length of a Mediterranean beach, or 6,000 tons per mile. The rate of transport was 1 knot. This figure gives some idea of the rate at which material is transported during storms.

Tidal Rise and Fall

As a result of tidal action there is a vertical movement of sea level which is in theory harmonic and has a period of about 12 hours 25 minutes. This general statement, however, needs qualification of many kinds; in the first place the movement is not always harmonic, secondly the amplitude varies widely from place to place and from day to day, and thirdly the period can vary either by minor variations of the astronomical interval of 12 hours 25 minutes, or it may be nearly either half or twice this amount.

Astronomical conditions decide whether the tides are springs—the maximum range which occurs fortnightly at about the time of full and new moon—or neaps, the minimum range which occurs midway between springs. The range also varies from place to place, and is much affected by the configuration of the coastline. As the tidal wave enters a funnel-shaped bay like the Bristol Channel or the Bay of Fundy the range increases rapidly, and the high tides at the heads of these two bays are well known. Fig. III.12 indicates the tidal range for six places in the Bristol Channel. Of the two figures in the brackets against each place the greater is the spring range in feet, and the smaller neap range. It will be seen that the range varies considerably over comparatively short distances; not only are the variations great, but they appear to be erratic. For instance, there is a considerable difference between the ranges at Ilfracombe and Watchet, while those at Barry and Cardiff are almost the same. It will also be seen that the spring range at Watchet is 4 feet greater than that at Ilfracombe, while it is 9 feet less than that at Avonmouth, which is at a comparable distance to the east. These examples should convince readers of the dangers of attempting to interpolate between published tidal data.

Before going further into the vagaries of tidal behaviour it is well to realize how these variations in tidal rise and fall affect the processes which are at work on the coastline. Clearly, it means that, when the tidal range is great, the agencies of erosion, deposition and transport are spread over a wide band, rather than concentrated on

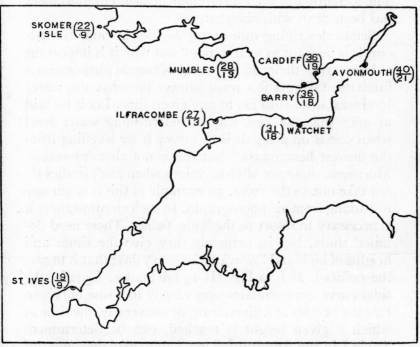

SKOMER $\left(\frac{22}{9}\right)$
ISLE

MUMBLES $\left(\frac{28}{13}\right)$ CARDIFF $\left(\frac{36}{19}\right)$ AVONMOUTH $\left(\frac{40}{21}\right)$

BARRY $\left(\frac{36}{18}\right)$

ILFRACOMBE $\left(\frac{27}{13}\right)$

$\left(\frac{31}{18}\right)$ WATCHET

ST IVES $\left(\frac{19}{9}\right)$

Fig. III.12.—Tidal ranges at stations in the Bristol Channel.

a narrow belt; the effect of this is more obvious of course on flat beaches than on rocky coasts or shingle banks. But the difference between a beach with a large tidal range, such as Woolacombe in Devon, and a beach in the South of France is very striking; the former is a wide expanse of clean sand, washed twice a day by the incoming tide, and planed flat by the action of waves and currents whose actions vary in magnitude and direction

73

almost hourly; the latter is, as it were, a sandy edge to a salt pond, the landward or sandy side of which is covered by water only in freak circumstances, and on which the paper bags and cigarette ends remain all too long, while below the water edge wave and current action are confined to a belt whose width is by comparison very small. The formation of the offshore bar in such circumstances has been dealt with elsewhere.

Before describing other irregularities in tidal behaviour, it is perhaps as well to point out why it is important to be aware of them. In any study of coastal phenomena a fundamental question must always be what the water level was, is, or is to be, at any given time. Let it be said at once that the best way of determining water level when one is on a beach is to survey it by levelling from the nearest benchmark;[1] but this is not always possible. Moreover, there are often occasions when one's studies do not take one to the coast; an example of this is when one is working from air photographs. In such circumstances it is necessary to resort to the Tide Tables. These need detailed study, but in principle they give the times and heights of high and low water for every day; that is to say, the points L H L in Fig. III.13 are known. Usually, the tidal curve approximates very closely to a sine curve, so that the heights at a given time, or conversely, the time at which a given height is reached, can be determined. Table I in the Admiralty Tide Tables explains how this can be done. But local conditions cause difficulties; for instance, at Le Havre there is a stand at high tide as is indicated by the pecked line in Fig. III.13. Clearly it is important that this should be taken into account: interpolation on a sine curve assumption between high and low water would give very misleading results for a place like Le Havre.

[1] The method would of course be impracticable if a rough sea were running.

In some places there are single day tides; that is, there may be only one high water and one low water a day; two high waters and two low waters may be regarded as normal; at Southampton as many as four high and four low waters may occur in a day.

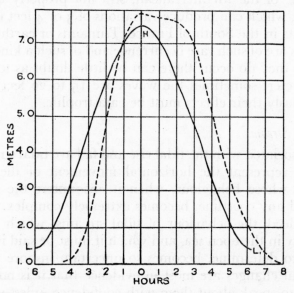

FIG. III.13.—Spring tide curves; continuous line Brest; broken line Le Havre.

Such phenomena are important, and clearly must be taken into account; freak phenomena have usually been investigated and tide level predictions published, they are therefore not likely to create any difficulty. Errors in tide heights are most commonly caused by ill-advised attempts to interpolate values between stations or by assuming that the rise and fall is harmonic when it is not.

One more difficulty in determining sea level at any given instant must be mentioned, that is variations due to meteorological and other causes. These may be considerable as has been shown on p. 34 and Fig. II.5.

Probably the best example is surges which are dealt with in pp. 79 et seq., in which attention is focused on the North Sea surges which are for obvious reasons of great importance in this country. But there are many other instances of such variations in level, notably 'Raz de marée' of the Mediterranean, still not properly understood, which can produce variations of 3 or 4 feet in tide heights in the South of France. Tsunamis or earthquake waves are of such rare occurrence and of such a kind that when they do occur there can be little doubt as to their character; sometimes the waves are 15 to 20 feet high; obviously their effects must be catastrophic.

Tidal Streams

Associated with the tidal rise and fall are tidal streams; these represent the horizontal movement of the tidal wave whose behaviour, when it encounters the shoals round any coastline, becomes extremely complex.

Indeed, the behaviour of tidal streams, which varies widely in the open sea, and which it must be said is difficult to determine, becomes so uncertain inshore where coastal changes are most in evidence that it is not possible to speak about them with confidence unless special observations for the purpose have been made. But since such observations are extremely rare, and, as is shown on p. 173, almost impossible, it is often necessary to use published information of tidal streams.

Information about them is given in the Admiralty Sailing Directions and more fully in special Charts and Atlases for the purpose; these latter usually indicate with arrows the directions of tidal streams at given times, or states of tide, and in figures the velocities at springs and neaps. Many navigational charts give more detailed tidal stream information for a few selected places; these places are indicated by diamonds enclosing the letter which gives reference to the marginal information.

The importance of tidal streams in coastal research is that they run roughly parallel to the coast, and are therefore able to transport material alongshore; that is to say in a direction roughly at right angles to the mean direction of wave action. Before dealing with the irregularities of tidal streams it is possible to outline some of their general characteristics. Normally they reverse their directions: that is to say, just as the tide rises and falls, so, if the tidal streams run south for six hours, it will normally run north for six hours,[1] with a period of slack water at the change. The velocity of the current will decrease inshore until at the edge of the water, especially on a flat sandy beach, it becomes quite small. The velocity at a given place also decreases with an increase in depth; that is to say, if there is a velocity of two knots on the surface, the velocity on the bottom where material is being moved will be much smaller.

It is when tidal streams encounter shoal water and an accidented coastline that their effects become very complex. When the stream is obstructed by any coastal feature its direction is changed either horizontally or vertically, and the velocity is altered. In passing a point, an eddy may be formed which in fact *reverses* the direction of the stream locally. If two streams meet eddies may be formed, and when the velocity is great and the configuration of the bed deflects the current upwards a *race* may occur; in such circumstances there would be heavy breaking seas, overfalls, and tide rips such as occur at Portland. There the spring velocity is sometimes as much as five knots. In the Corrievreckan between the islands of Jura and Scarba on the West Coast of Scotland the velocities are higher, and it is said that in the Pentland Firth streams of eleven knots occur.

It is rarely possible, in a detailed study of a specific

[1] The periods of ebb and flow can be very erratic; no better account of the behaviour of tidal streams can be given than in the Admiralty Atlases.

erosion problem, to separate the longshore effects of tidal streams from those of currents (oceanic), local currents due to wind, and the longshore component of oblique wave action. All are contributory factors of the total longshore movement which is responsible for removing the material from one place where it has been eroded and stirred into suspension by wave action to another where it is deposited, probably temporarily when the storm is over; or perhaps, in rare cases, permanently.

An excellent example of the effect of tidal streams is provided by Hurst Spit; here the east–west effect of the streams in Christchurch Bay is obvious and explains the eastward growth of the spit; but to the eastward end it comes under the influence of the powerful streams in the Solent, and there is little doubt that the bank known as the Shingles, south-west of Hurst Castle, consists of material carried there from the end of Hurst Spit by the ebb streams in the Solent.

Currents

Most ocean currents are closely associated with the world wind circulation, and for this reason they are dealt with in Chapter IV. They quite clearly provide a source of transport; their effect is just the same as that of tidal streams; that is to say if they encounter material in suspension they will carry it along. They differ from tidal streams in that in general their directions are constant; they are never reversible. Their action inshore is never spectacular, and is not often important.

They are not, however, entirely negligible. Recent researches in the North Sea, the results of which are summarized in the *Atlas of Tides and Tidal Streams— British Islands and Adjacent Waters—Charts Number 5044– 5056,* indicate that on the East Coast of England the north-going and south-going tidal streams nearly balance; but there appears to be a residual movement of a more permanent kind which is almost certainly associated with the Gulf Stream to the north. It is this residual current which may well explain the southward material at such points as Yarmouth and Orfordness.

It would be unwise to be dogmatic in these matters; our methods of observation are not yet sufficiently advanced to distinguish in detail the individual factors of current, tide and wave action which combine to cause coastal drifting. We cannot yet measure the resultant longshore water movement regardless of whether it be due to current or tide when the seas are rough. Current measurements made inshore so far are inadequate and unreliable for our purposes and those who make them are probably most suspicious of them.

METEOROLOGICAL EFFECTS

Local Wind Effects

Apart from the generation of waves by wind there are other meteorological conditions of a temporary nature which produce considerable and important effects.

First, the wind tends to create a current in the direction in which it is blowing. In consequence sea level is raised in the direction towards which the current, so generated, is running. Obviously sea level cannot rise unless there is a current running towards the area where the level is rising. Variations in sea level due to this cause rarely exceed one foot in open water. These local, short-term currents can be of great importance in attempting to explain erosion problems.

Surges

A change in the barometric pressure will produce a change in the level of the sea. If we imagine a large 'level' ocean, with a column of air over one part of it heavier than that over the surrounding water, obviously the heavier air will depress the sea level more than the lighter surrounding air. If the barometer rises one inch, or 34 millibars, sea level is depressed by about one foot; if the barometer falls an inch, the level is likely to rise about a foot. These figures are to be considered a general guide; in fact the changes are often slow, irregular, and variable. See Fig. II.5.

Vertical movements of the order of one foot *in the open sea* are comparatively unimportant, for effective waves are much more than one foot in height; so that the part of the beach subject to the process of erosion is determined more by wave height than by a comparatively small variation in sea level. The importance of meteorological effects is when the seas are partially enclosed, for then the effect is greatly enhanced, and no better example of this phenomenon can be quoted than the surges which occur in the North Sea. The following account is taken from the *Introduction to the Admiralty Tide Tables* (*European Waters*).

'Meteorological conditions have a very considerable effect upon sea level in the southern part of the North Sea, particularly in the Wash and Thames Estuary, along the intervening coast, and on the Netherlands coast. On occasions the sea has been raised to more than seven feet above its predicted high water levels and on others has fallen to more than four feet below its predicted low water levels. *Tides which rise or fall two to three feet above or below the predicted high or low water levels are not infrequent.*

'In general northerly winds raise sea level by driving water southwards into the narrowed confines of the southern part of the North Sea, and to a lesser extent southerly winds lower sea level by expelling water from the southern North Sea.

'On 31 January 1953 a northerly gale of exceptional strength and duration, blowing over the whole of the North Sea, raised sea level by nine feet on the east coast of

England, and raised it even higher on the Netherlands coast. On this occasion the level was raised by a large amount for over twelve hours and as the gale occurred during a period of spring tides disastrous flooding occurred when the tide was high. The predicted high water heights were exceeded by nearly eight feet on the coast between the Rivers Humber and Thames, and by more than ten feet on part of the Netherlands coast.

'The most favourable conditions for lowering sea level occur when a large deep depression is situated well to the north-west of Ireland, either stationary or moving slowly to the north-east. The associated winds over the North Sea are then southerly or, in the extreme south, are south-westerly.

'The most favourable conditions for raising sea level in the southern part of the North Sea occur when a deep depression has moved over to the eastward of the North Sea and lies over Scandinavia or Northern Germany. The associated winds over the North Sea are northerly, or, in the extreme north, are north-westerly.

'The largest changes in sea level occur when conditions favourable to lowering sea level are fairly abruptly replaced by those with the opposite tendency, as when a depression travels quickly across the northern part of the North Sea. The rapid change in wind direction sets up an oscillation which raises and lowers sea level by amounts greater than those directly attributable to the wind force. The periods, however, for which the wind is raised or lowered by the maximum amounts are comparatively brief and in consequence the effects of these oscillations are generally dangerous only if the peak occurs near high tide, or the trough near low tide. It was to these oscillations that the term "Storm Surge" was originally applied but it is now commonly used in reference to any elevation of sea level due to meteorological conditions. In the Thames Estuary a surge with a peak over twelve feet high has been recorded, and on another occasion one with a maximum depression of over six feet was recorded. There is no record, however, either of the peak of such an extreme surge coinciding with high tide, or of such an extreme depression with low tide.'

The North Sea surge has been quoted as one which occurs close at hand, and one that is not difficult to understand. Some meteorological effects, however, at present defy explanation; indeed Corkan has said that 'A more complete understanding of how the meteorological tide is produced and the discovery of a satisfactory method of predicting it are probably the most important practical problems relating to tides awaiting solution'. To illustrate this, and in order to counter the fallacious idea that the level of the sea is always raised when the local wind is onshore, he refers to the paper published by Dr. Doodson in 1924. This paper includes a diagram, Fig. III.14, showing the most effective winds for raising sea level at places on the British coasts. This diagram reveals a most surprising state of affairs; for example, at Felixstowe the most effective direction may be nearly offshore.

Much research, notably by the Liverpool Observatory and Tidal Institute, has been devoted to the examination of surge phenomena, and in particular to predicting the height and time of arrival of surge waves at vulnerable points. A first indication that a surge is likely to occur is the meteorological chart; actual evidence that it is in existence comes from tide gauges. On Fig. III.15 the pecked line shows the theoretical or predicted curve for Southend during the surge of 31 January–1 February of 1953. Superimposed on this is the actual trace from the tide gauge. The difference between these two traces— plotted on the lowest curve—represents the amount of the surge. Observations of past surges show that the rate of travel of the surge wave is regular and therefore

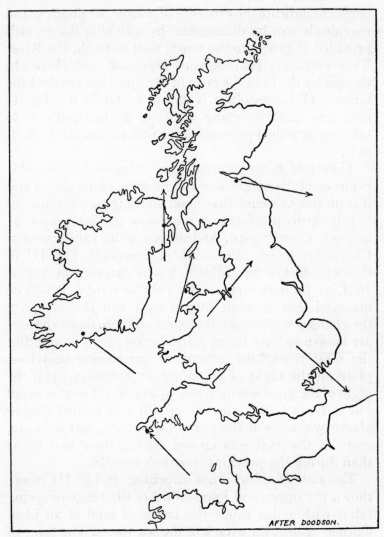

Fig. III.14.—The most effective winds for raising sea level at places on British coasts.

predictable; if, therefore, the tide gauge at Aberdeen begins to indicate the existence of a surge, its progress and magnitude can be determined by watching the records provided at gauges to the south, such as Leith, the River Tyne entrance, Immingham, Lowestoft and Harwich; though by the time the crest of the surge has reached the latitude of Lowestoft it is almost certainly too late to issue any useful warning to places further south or to take any practical precautions against the harmful effects of it.

These tide gauge records, however, provide invaluable evidence of the magnitude and progress of the surge; and it is on this evidence that flood warnings are given.

It is hardly possible to overestimate the part played by surges in coast erosion. An instance of this can be seen at Covehithe, seven miles south of Lowestoft. Fig. III.16 shows profiles of the cliff which were surveyed in August 1951, 31 January 1953, and 1 February 1953. It will be observed that between August 1951 and January 1953 the changes were small, though even these small changes are known to have taken place during minor surges. But the most remarkable change is the erosion that took place on the night of 31 January–1 February 1953, the night of the great storm, when 35 feet of cliff were washed away. In fact, this amount of cliff was eroded during about two hours at the peak of the surge; that is to say, more of this cliff was eroded during these two hours than during the previous seventeen months.

This state of affairs is not surprising. In Fig. III.16 are shown the upper and lower limits of the range of spring tides; within this range the beach of sand is an ideal defence against the attack of the sea waves. The force of these waves, spread over a breaker zone 60 feet wide, is at no point severe, and the surface of sand is virtually indestructible. Thus the waves may batter themselves against this belt of beach without causing any change

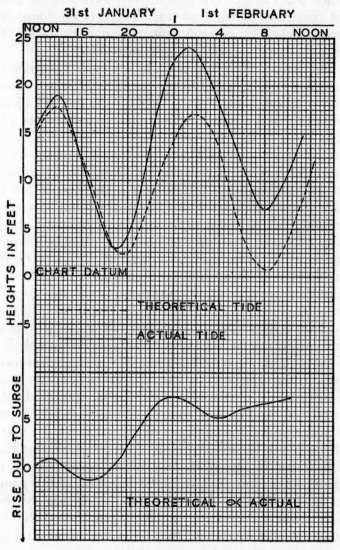

FIG. III.15.—Actual and predicted tide curves for Southend—31 January and 1 February 1953.

which is not likely to be remedied by some slightly different condition of wind or tide. There is no doubt that sand beaches are nature's best reply to the attack of the sea until some unusual factor is introduced.

The surge, however, is such a factor. Consider the conditions of this night in 1953: the surge raised the sea level by about 8 feet—to the level of S on Fig. III.16, and the crests of the waves, which could not have been less than 10 or 12 feet in height, reached a height W; and it has to be remembered that the waves were of unprecedented violence. Because of their height and because of the surge, they were attacking not the beach, but the cliff of sand which is very soft, and which has an angle of rest of about 45°. The cliff was rapidly undercut, and it then collapsed, this process being repeated at frequent intervals; the longshore movement of the water rapidly transported it away from the zone of the cliffs. It is difficult to imagine conditions more favourable to rapid erosion.

There is little doubt that surges, raising the level of the wave attack above the beach to a more vulnerable land formation, play a very large part in many cases of severe erosion; the effect can be seen at Dunwich, on the coasts of Yorkshire and Norfolk, and there is little doubt that erosion on our Channel coast is due in no small measure to this cause. For instance, there is strong evidence that at Christchurch the damage done to the cliffs during most of the year is negligible, but during severe storms the results are obvious; unfortunately the siting of tide gauges on the English side of the Channel is such that we know little about surges there, but there is unmistakable evidence of other kinds that they do in fact occur, and that erosion is accelerated because of them.

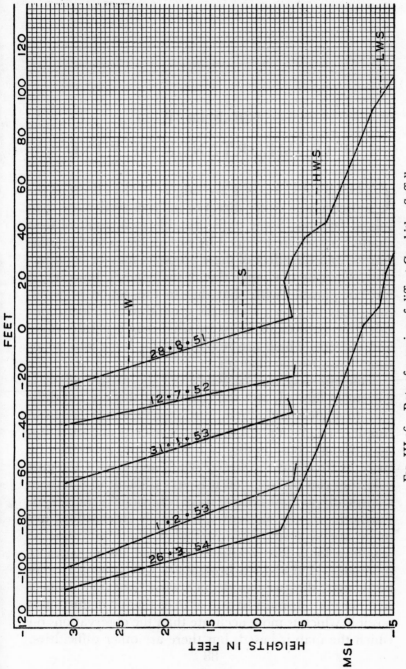

FIG. III.16.—Rate of recession of cliffs at Covehithe, Suffolk.

CHAPTER IV

THE IMPORTANCE OF WIND

COASTAL features are subject to the effects of the atmosphere either direct or indirect even more than inland features. Some cliffs crumble as a result of frost shatter; others are reduced by surface creep during rainstorms, and the effect of these processes may be considerable. The rate of change due to such causes, however, is not comparable with that due to the action of wind. Sand may be blown above the ground so as to form considerable features, or the same wind may generate waves and currents which are responsible for large and sometimes catastrophic changes.

Unfortunately our knowledge of the earth's winds is extremely limited, and the reasons for this are not difficult to understand. First, the observation is far from simple. At a given point the wind's velocity and direction may change considerably in a short time; gusts may be twice as strong as the steady wind, and even if the gust velocities can be recorded it is very difficult to use them statistically, at least as far as wave behaviour is concerned. Furthermore, the stations where such observations are made are very sparsely distributed; there are none at sea, save for a few weather ships. And the vagaries of monsoons, land and sea breezes are well known. It may be thought that we can deduce wind behaviour from a weather map. It must be said at once that no deduction is possible which is more accurate than the observations on which the map is based, but there are other difficulties.

88

The isobars of the map are often interpolated between sparse pressure values, and these pressures may be changing rapidly. Thus we are dealing with winds which vary between the softness of a summer zephyr and the steadiness of trade winds upon which the old sailing ships used to depend, and the savage typhoon with its speeds up to 100 m.p.h., its changes in direction, and its sudden onset and calm at the centre.

Wind then is the source of energy for nearly all coastal changes. It can move material directly by blowing sand from place to place, or indirectly by generating currents which transport material in suspension, or by creating waves which are of the greatest importance among coastal processes. In order to obtain a clearer understanding of what is going on we will consider these three processes one at a time, meanwhile being careful to remember that the parts played by them become inextricably involved in almost every problem that we may wish to study. Currents would rarely do harm were there no waves to raise the sea bed into suspension, and the damage done by waves would be relatively small if there were no currents to remove the material that they had eroded.

Waves

The importance of wind is apparent when we realize that it is wind alone which is responsible for the generation of waves whose action is certainly the most important factor in coastal changes.

The experts on wave behaviour are of two kinds; the mathematicians who regard it as a hydrodynamic problem which should admit of a mathematical explanation, and those who use what may be called statistical methods in order to elicit an understanding of wave behaviour from the many observations that have been made.

Both investigators, and particularly the second category, are dependent upon observations, and here a difficulty arises, for many of the observations used have been unreliable. Only comparatively recently have wave tanks, in which accurate measurements can be made, been available; hitherto all the data came from workers who, to the best of their ability, had made their observations from beaches or other vantage points on the coast. The determination of these men calls for our highest praise and their integrity is beyond question, but their difficulties were insuperable. Waves are not well defined, and they move rapidly, so that heights and lengths were only roughly assessed. The same applies to their velocities; sometimes a fairly constant period can be seen, but often even this is not evident because several wave systems may be running at the same time. Nor do the difficulties end here; if the object of the investigation is to discover something about the creation, or generation of the waves, it is necessary to have information about the wind responsible for them; its strength, duration and direction, and distance from the observer. As a rule only the roughest estimates of these quantities can be made. It is not necessary to explain that the waves which are seen are not necessarily the result of local winds, but very probably of winds blowing over an area many miles away.

Very many observations have been made, and they have been examined with much thoroughness and care. Not all the results agree, but from among the numerous authorities some useful conclusions have been reached.

In general terms the result of the observations made may be summarized as follows:

If a wind of a given velocity blows for an infinite time, or over an infinite distance—there is a theoretical maximum wave height—and wave period—that it can generate. Until these maxima are reached, the following general conditions can be stated:

(I) For a wind of a given strength the wave height increases with an increase in the distance over which the wind has blown.

(II) The longer a wind of given strength blows, the faster do the waves move, and at the same time the lengths, and therefore the periods, of the waves increase.

(III) For a wind blowing over a given distance, the harder it blows the higher will the waves be.

(IV) For a wind blowing over a given distance, the harder it blows, the greater will the velocity of the waves become; their lengths and periods will also gradually increase.

These conditions are stated quantitatively in appendices C and D which should be carefully studied.

CURRENTS

Some horizontal water movements are due to the density distribution in the sea, and some to tidal behaviour.

The former are relatively unimportant in coastal problems; the effect of tidal streams has been discussed elsewhere. But there is another kind of water movement which is of importance, namely wind currents. These must be considered as of two kinds; first the great ocean currents, and secondly the local currents which, inshore, are of greater importance than the fringe effect of the great oceanic streams.

When the wind blows on the ocean it exerts a stress which carries a surface layer along with it, and this layer will tend to take a lower layer with it, and so on. At the same time the effect of Coriolis force is to turn currents to the right in the northern hemisphere, and to the left in the southern. The amount of this deflection from the direction of the wind can be considerable; it can be 45°

on the surface, and it increases with depth—the velocity meanwhile decreasing with depth—until a point can be reached when the water is travelling in a direction opposite to that of the wind.

As we are concerned with the inshore effects of currents, the following extract from the introduction to the Admiralty Tide Tables is of interest; after discussing storm surges in the North Sea, it goes on: 'The Meteorological conditions which give rise to these variations in mean sea level have also their effect upon the horizontal water movements. These conditions which cause a raising of sea level in the North Sea bring about a current flowing from the North Sea into the English Channel, while a lowering of sea level in the North Sea will be associated with a current flowing in the opposite direction. The south-west-going current, which may reach a rate of three-quarters of a knot, will be apparent as an increase in the duration and rate of the south-west-going flow in Dover Strait, with a corresponding decrease in the duration and rate of the north-east-going flow.

'Generally speaking no data are available regarding the rate which a current may be expected to attain in a partially enclosed sea; it is, however, considered unlikely that a rate of about 1 knot is often exceeded. As with changes in sea level, the current increases in rate slowly to a maximum, depending on the force of the wind, decreases slowly when the wind decreases, and may continue to run after the wind has ceased. The current begins on the surface, and, as it increases, gradually penetrates down below the surface, but, unless of very long duration, probably never reaches any great depth. Its direction in open water is, as has been stated, usually, when facing the direction towards which the wind is blowing, rather to the right of that direction (in the northern hemisphere), but the direction may be

92

changed by land or shoals. The current on and near the surface usually sets up a counter current, which may run below it, or on both sides of it; thus it may happen that the current below, say 10 fathoms, is running in a direction opposite to that on the surface, but no rule or even probability regarding this can be given. . . .'

The complex behaviour of these currents at depth has little bearing on what happens on beaches: but action of the surface currents is relevant to our problem, even bearing in mind the fact that the velocity falls off rapidly inshore, so that the water movement on a beach due to such currents would never appear very impressive. It is possible, however, that the southward trends of the mouth of the Yare and of the spit at Orfordness are to some extent due to a current which is due to wind action, for as far as can be judged at many points on this coast the ebb and flow of the tides is very nearly balanced.

It has been said that it is desirable that the principles of wave generation should be understood, and the formulae that have been quoted are useful in forming general assessments of what kind of wave might be expected to be found at a given place. Equally, published current charts are useful records of the mean general flow over long periods. But it would be dangerous to use evidence of this kind for specific detailed studies of small coastal problems. Current charts, for instance, are almost invariably on scales so small that it is impossible to deduce the retardation due to the shoaling of the sea bed inshore, nor can they convey the effects of irregularities in the coastline or of rapidly varying winds. If a given problem requires accurate knowledge of currents, then direct observations must be made; no argument from first principles can take the place of first-hand measurements. It would be equally unsatisfactory to try to deduce wave dimensions from wind measurements. Such a course

H

might be justifiable during a war when direct measurement is impossible, but accurate results are clearly not possible by these means. Meteorological stations are sparse on land; they are virtually non-existent at sea, so that the quantities to be substituted in the formulae are not sufficiently well known for reliable calculations.

Local effects can be of great importance. On the East Coast of Britain the longshore movement is very largely governed by the direction of onshore winds blowing at the time. Current observations made with floats in the neighbourhood of Lowestoft have frequently shown that *inshore*, that is, in less than a fathom of water, the movement goes with the wind rather than with the tide. The effect of local wind could not of course overwhelm very powerful streams such as those at Portland or Pentland.

The effect of such local winds is of two kinds; first the creation of a longshore wind-blown current, and secondly the generation of oblique waves, and these two effects become almost inextricably inter-related. There is no practical advantage in trying to separate the two actions; indeed it is convenient to analyse the effects, due to both causes, along the two axes parallel to, and normal to, the coastline. Float observations will indicate the rate of drift in the former direction, and the wave dimensions, considered along with the beach gradients, will decide where the constructive and destructive zones are, and consequently the nature of the movement normal to the coastline.

THE EFFECT OF OFFSHORE WINDS

Coastlines exposed to strong gales from the sea like Seaford or Selsea must inevitably suffer erosion; the gales which they experience from the south-west will cause heavy surf, and, as has been seen, such seas are destructive. By contrast, beaches whose prevailing winds are strong from an offshore direction may benefit very greatly. When the wind blows strongly to seaward, the upper layer of water is carried with it, and if equilibrium is to be preserved there will be a reverse current *landwards*, and this must be on or near the sea bed. The water circulation is similar to that of cold water coasts. If, when this kind of circulation is in being there is sand in suspension near the sea bed, it must obviously be carried shoreward. During an offshore wind wave action is likely to be slight; destructive waves could hardly occur, so that the whole movement of bed material is likely to be shoreward.

This effect *must* therefore exist when the prevailing winds are offshore; in many areas other agencies, such as surges or longshore drifting, outweigh its positive action, but there are places where its importance is apparent. At Seaton Delaval, south of Blyth in Northumberland, it is well known that the onset of offshore winds causes the arrival of large banks of sand which appear first at the level of low tide, and then, if the wind continues long enough, progress steadily landwards towards the back of the beach. This effect has been clearly shown by surveying the beach profile at frequent intervals. Thus, if erosive conditions have lowered the level of the beach, or if, as sometimes happens, large amounts of sand are removed by contractors, the deficiency will be made good by a week of offshore winds. We shall see later that the benefits of this process may be still further enhanced by a shift of the wind which will transport the sand thus pulled from the sea bed to the zone at the back of the beach where dunes are formed.

SURGES

Surges have been dealt with in Chapter III. They are, of course, brought about entirely by the action of wind.

WIND-BLOWN SAND

The coastline is not moulded by hydraulic agencies alone; it is true that the final distribution of material at the water's edge is usually (but not quite always) made by the action of water, but this material, once it has emerged from the sea, may then be transported above the land, and for short distances above water, by wind action. And it is wind which, once currents and waves have raised a shingle ridge high enough above sea level, can cover it with sand, thus contriving to make a considerable feature. Many readers will have suffered the discomfort of stinging sand on knees or face, when walking on a dry beach on a very windy day. The writer remembers one evening at Ostend when the sand was blowing so fiercely on an otherwise pleasant evening that not a soul was to be seen on the beach. King [2] found that a beach in the South of France changed appreciably due to this cause, and that in water depths up to 3 feet deposits of some inches were made in a few hours. This is not surprising, for a simple sand trapping measurement showed that when the wind was blowing at 24 m.p.h. sand was moving at the rate of 0·2 lb. per minute per foot front, and this is three-quarters of a hundredweight per day; with a stronger wind the rate of transport would be greater, so that over a beach a mile long 200 tons might be moved in a day.

The process of transporting sand by wind has been dealt with exhaustively by Bagnold: the action which blows sand near the sea is very similar to that which is at work in the desert, with the difference that in the desert the wind blows over an area which can be assumed to be infinitely great, while coastal dunes must be regarded as fringing features, so that the orientation of the beach relative to prevailing, or strong winds, is a matter of considerable importance.

The means by which wind moves sand fall under two broad headings; the first, commonly called sand creep, occurs when the wind pressure on grains causes them to roll without leaving the surface; the effect of this rolling is that a thin layer of the surface of the sand moves steadily, but slowly, with the wind. 'Creep' takes place when the wind velocities are small. As the wind becomes stronger the side pressure increases and the action becomes more violent: the lateral push causes grains to roll with such violence that a time comes when the impact causes them to jump; once they are in mid-air the horizontal effect of the wind is greater, so that the grains move by jumps, or 'saltations'. During this process grains usually rise to a height of about 12 or 18 inches, the latter being about the maximum height for simple saltations. Higher trajectories than this, which are not infrequently experienced on beaches and among dunes—for the sand is often driven into one's eyes—are almost certainly explained by a rebound of one grain from another in mid-air.

A perfect bounce causes a jump of unusual size, so that a few grains may rise much higher than the ordinary height of saltation: but the amount of sand moving at these heights is relatively small. Ripples are often found on sand surfaces, but their existence is not a matter of great importance.

The rate of sand transport can be measured by means of traps.

Fig. IV.1A shows a trap for measuring the rate of movement by saltation; the sand enters the slots on the face CD, and falls into the container E. Thus the amount of sand moving in the section of the trap per unit of time can be observed. It is to be noticed that the very existence of the trap must deform the air flow in its vicinity, and the determination must for this reason be to some extent imperfect.

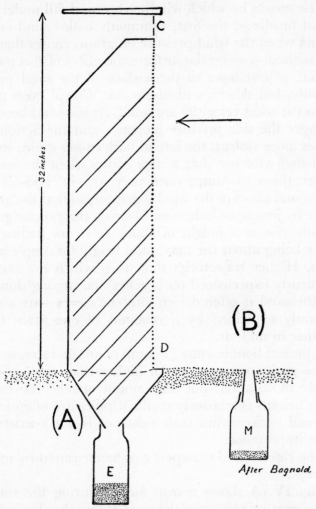

FIG. IV.1.—Sand Collectors; A. Saltation trap; B. Trap for surface creep.

In Fig. IV.1B trap M is sunk in the sand with its rectangular neck level with the sand surface; this neck is so small and narrow that it is unlikely to collect grains which are moved by saltation, but those which creep along the surface will fall in. Thus the amount of sand moving along a path the width of the neck of the trap can be measured for a unit of time.

The optimum conditions for the blowing of sand on a coastline are a wide beach, with dry sand, and a strong wind. If the wind is along the length of the beach the rate of transport will be at its greatest, though the effect of the transport in terms of sand deposits may not be apparent. These optimum conditions are not common; if the tidal rise and fall is small, the beach will be narrow; the beach will also be narrow if its gradient is steep. Some beaches dry very slowly; if the hinterland drains into the beach sand, it may never dry. Sand will blow more freely if there are deposits of sand, whether dune or otherwise, above the level of high springs, but it is to be assumed that these were at some time derived from the foreshore, so that we shall consider them a *result* rather than a cause of blowing.

Deposits of sand at the back of beaches are usually in the form of dunes, though they are sometimes flat. If the area of sand is large, dunes are almost certain to exist, and it is easier to explain the existence of dunes than that of large flat areas of dry sand. The wide backs of beaches near Narbonne in the South of France, for instance, may owe their flatness to the Raz de Marée which destroy any embryo dunes as soon as their formation begins.

In desert conditions, where wind behaviour follows a regular pattern, and when the wind from any direction can carry sand, the dunes are usually of two kinds; the crescentic pattern known as 'barchans' or those of an elongated or swordshaped form known as 'seifs'. Bagnold has explained how both kinds of dune are formed. It is because of the special circumstances in which they are situated that coastal dunes are rarely of one of these two kinds. Coastal dunes have the sea on one side (or more); they may lie near very uneven topography, and the source of their sand may be very localized. Thus, while the circumstances responsible for the accumulation of sand as dunes may be simply explained, there is little point in attempting a detailed examination of their forms in detail; local conditions can vary so widely that the dunes themselves appear as almost haphazard mounds of sand, although occasionally in large dune areas something approaching the desert patterns may occasionally be seen.

The existence of dunes then can usually be explained thus; first a wind blows shorewards across a beach of dry sand, taking both by creep and saltation a load of sand with it. At the end of the expanse of sand a rougher surface is encountered, either of pebbles or vegetation, and here the sand is deposited. Once a ridge of sand has been formed, the character of the wind-flow is changed so that the dune-form is developed by deposition on the forward face of the mound. The subsequent increase in height is usually accelerated by the growth of vegetation which is usually of two kinds; one when the dune height is small, so that the plants are rooted in the sub-dune material, and the other when the height of the dunes is considerable. At this stage marram grass is the commonest dune plant, though there are a number of others in this country. The importance of marram grass is twofold; first the foliage retards the wind velocity and so causes the deposit of sand, and secondly the long roots have a binding effect on the sand, and so serve to stabilize the dunes. Bagnold writes '—as long as the vegetation is alive, the surface on which it grows cannot ever become fully charged with sand, for the grass grows higher as the sand around it accumulates. The result is that under all wind conditions the grassy surface acts as a continuous deposition area, and we get great undulating tracts of accumulated sand such as the gozes of Kordofan, which are devoid of steepsided dunes.' Coastal dunes are rarely completely covered by vegetation, and steep slip-slopes or blow-outs do in fact occur. Dune heights in this country rarely exceed 60 feet, though at Culbin a height of 100 feet is reached. In the Baltic there are dunes 150 and 160 feet high, and one dune in Holland reaches a height of over 250 feet.

Little is to be gained from a study of dune *forms*. It has already been said that the conditions of sand movement are much more restricted than those in a large desert, so that recurring barchans or seifs are unlikely to be formed; but further, the initial deposits are to a very great extent predetermined by the configuration of the terrain at the back of the beach. At Scolt, for instance, the dunes have tended to follow the shingle ridges. The movement after this stage will depend upon highly accidental factors such as the rate of colonization by dune plants, the availability of sand, and the artificial destruction of the plant cover by animals or human agencies. At Culbin sands the area of dune is so great that desert forms have almost developed, and, indeed, the sand area began to invade the neighbouring areas so that considerable control works had to be undertaken.

When dunes are not anchored by vegetation they can move at an appreciable rate; it is recorded that in the Bay of Biscay, with prevailing south-westerly winds the rate of movement has been 16 feet per annum, and in Denmark speeds of from 3 to 24 feet per annum have been recorded. Bagnold has computed than on a barchan dune 15 metres high a wind of 30 miles per hour would move 0·46 tons per hour, and that this corresponds to an advance by the whole dune of 1·8 cm. per hour; for smaller shrinking dunes the rate of advance would be much faster.

The value of dunes in protecting a coastline from erosion is indirect. A heap of sand offers little resistance to the action of destructive waves; this has been very clearly demonstrated on our East Coast in Suffolk where, since the floods of 1953, banks of sand and shingle have been bulldozed at the back of the beach in order—it was hoped—to hold back the sea. In effect, once the waves reached them they were washed away. Dunes would suffer the same fate *if the waves reached them*, but they appear to protect themselves, and the coastline on which they are situated, because of their influence on the wave behaviour to seaward of them. The dunes represent an accumulation or capital asset of sand, which, if it has been derived from the beaches, is available to be returned thither from time to time, so that the existence of dunes is likely to help to preserve the amount of sand in the area as a whole, and therefore on the neighbouring beaches. It is not claimed that this must always be so; but there are good reasons for believing it to be the case for many dune areas.

One such area has been studied in some detail. There is a large area of dune between Seaton Sluice and Blyth in Northumberland. In general the coastline appears to be static, but at the southern end dunes have been flattened out, and the area has been built up on or turned into car parks and open land. The consequence has been erosion at that particular point. The reason seems to be clear; where sand is blown to the back of the beach it cannot stay there as dune but is blown further inland or swept from the roads, so that it is lost to that particular piece of coastline within the zone of beach changes. There can be little doubt that this loss accounts for the loss of the coastline by erosion, for the sand which has gone from the beach zone would formerly have been caught by the dunes and hence it could have been returned to the sea by suitable offshore winds, and so have been deposited on the beach once again.

Dunes, then, represent a capital of material which is of great value in maintaining a coastline. They should be encouraged, fostered, and protected. The public should be made to understand that to destroy the vegetation on them is to aggravate the nuisance of blowing sand, and, indirectly, to accelerate erosion of the neighbouring coastline.

coastline.

CHAPTER V

SOME COASTAL FORMS AND CHANGES

EARLIER chapters in this book have attempted to
deal with the geological factors which affect coastal
features, and with the agencies which work upon the
material of the coastline; which break it down, raise it
into suspension in the sea, or transport it from one place
to another.

The time has now come to study both of these considerations together, and to see how far they help us to
understand some of the features that we observe, and
some of the changes that are known to be taking place.
Sometimes coastal phenomena admit of clear and
acceptable explanations *qualitatively*; that is to say in the
manner of their formation and behaviour; but the rate
of change or quantitative analysis is more difficult. It
has already been pointed out that observation of the
processes in detail is often impossible.

On the other hand, some features are difficult to
explain at all, notably those which are dependent in
some way upon vertical movements of the sea or land.
Our knowledge of the precise sequence, magnitude or
speed of eustatic and isostatic movements is so meagre
that it is not possible to say with any degree of confidence
how certain results have been achieved. There is room
for speculation over a very wide field, but it has to be
admitted that it is not yet known what the sequence of
events has been. The best that we can do is to put forward

theories. Fortunately this theorizing is called for more often in connection with old formations such as barrier islands where the processes of formation which occurred in the geological past are matters of purely academic interest. Present changes, such as erosion forms, admit of a more precise treatment for the obvious reason that because the changes are taking place before our eyes they can within the limits of our observational powers be examined and measured.

There are good reasons for dividing our enquiries into these two categories; first the past, obscure, and inevitably subject to surmise or speculation, and the present which can be satisfactorily resolved when our observational skills have been successfully developed. Many changes which have taken place in the geological past may never be explained, though speculation about them is a proper exercise for students of such phenomena; but present changes are a challenge which must be taken up. If our observational resources do not yet lead us to a proper understanding of all of them we must improve our methods and rigorously apply them so that the forces which threaten our coastlines may be contained.

The Parabolic Beach Profile

It is sometimes assumed that a typical profile of a sandy beach is a parabola. The reason for this assumption appears to be that a large number of beaches are not simple inclined planes; the discernible curvature is rarely uniform over the beach, so that the profile is not bow-shaped or part of a circle; very often the gradient is steeper at the top of the beach than lower down; it is in this sense that the profile can be said to approximate to the parabolic form rather than to other geometrical curves.

We shall see later that in a simple wave tank it is

difficult to produce a beach of this shape, certainly they do not exist in tideless seas; but it is convenient and justifiable in studying the behaviour of beaches to consider this parabolic form as a kind of mean or basic pattern about which changes take place, or upon which minor variations are sometimes superimposed.

The infinitely varying range of beach profiles, which the reader can demonstrate quite easily from his own reading or observation, is ample reason for using the word 'parabolic' in this context with caution. As has been stated above, beaches are usually (but by no means always) steeper at the water's edge than in, say 2 or 3 fathoms. Also wave action tends to smooth out the sand, so that very often a profile which is nearly parabolic is formed. Typical of this are many Atlantic beaches in Cornwall and Devon where wave action is powerful, and the tidal range fairly large. The reason for the relative steepness at the water's edge is probably because here there is more surf than anywhere else, so that over a long period there is a subtraction or extraction of material. Lower down the beach constructive forces are more often at work, which tend to bring sand from seaward.

We shall therefore retain the notion of a parabolic profile (though realizing that particular conditions cause many departures from it), and we shall use it as a starting point for our brief study of profile changes. But it must be clearly understood that what follows is a simplification of what undoubtedly occurs. At any given time and place the processes may be so numerous and so complex that any individual factor may be obscured by others. We therefore conveniently ignore many factors in order to get a clearer understanding of the few.

Summer and Winter Profiles

If we assume that the sea is rougher in winter than in summer the beach gradients will vary between the seasons. The designations 'summer' and 'winter' are used because they appear in the literature; it would be more precise to talk of 'storm' and 'calm' profiles. This effect is described on p. 64.

The resultant 'oscillation' of the gradient of the upper half of the beach is a matter of common occurrence, but, for obvious reasons, it is most clearly seen on beaches where there is a small range of tide. The combing down effect is very rapid where there is a large shingle content in the beach material, because such material moves freely. At Covehithe in Suffolk it not infrequently happens that a storm lasting over one tide will lower the top of a beach by three feet; leaving the clayey beds exposed. A spell of calmer conditions will restore the beach to its former state, but this process may take days or weeks, because the energy of the small waves is small compared with that of the storm waves. The effect of a storm on the back of a beach of sand can be seen on Plate III.

Denudation of Beaches

There have been remarkable instances of the denudation of the upper levels of beaches by the process which causes the gradient oscillation referred to above, and sometimes the degree of denudation is so great that the return to normal is delayed for long periods. A remarkable instance was the removal of the entire covering of sand from many of the beaches in Normandy after storms at Easter 1950. (See Bourcart and Auzel.) At Deauville, the well-known resort, no sand was left, and at one stage the authorities transported sand to the beach in order to provide a local covering of the mud and peat which was almost everywhere exposed. There is no record of what happened to the eroded sand, but there can be little doubt that it was pulled seaward under the surf during a storm, probably accompanied by a surge.

The amount of sand removed was so great that it was not returned by subsequent constructive waves for two years.

This process of removal takes place on shingle beaches at a far more rapid rate than on sand beaches; a fact which is often not realized because shingle beaches are usually much thicker than sand beaches and changes are therefore less obvious. For whereas shingle banks may be tens of feet thick, the layer of sand on sandy beaches is usually of the order of a foot. It therefore happens that while the sand of a beach is often removed from small areas revealing the underlying formation, the formations below shingle are rarely uncovered except at the lower edge.

The 'Swash' Bar

This term has been applied to a bar which can be made in a wave tank by causing constructive waves to attack a flat sandy beach. In such circumstances there will be no breakers, with the result that the waves run up the beach, gradually losing height; they return thence partly by percolation, and partly as a very thin sheet of water whose movement is comparatively slow. Such conditions are of course typical of fair weather and calm seas.

If AA' represents the initial beach the movement of the bed material will be in the direction shown by the arrow in Fig. V.1 and before long the swash bar B will appear whose crest is at a height above water level which is determined by the upper limit of wave action; that is to say, the waves run up to B with a small load of sand. The bar B is thus formed by repeated depositions by these waves, and a small hollow L which is usually filled with water appears behind it.

It has been suggested that this process is responsible for building the bars between lagoons and the sea like those near Sète in the South of France or the Nehrungen in the Baltic, but such a conclusion is impossible for a number of reasons only one of which need be mentioned here. The process which can build a swash bar is extremely gentle, and for obvious reasons the feature can

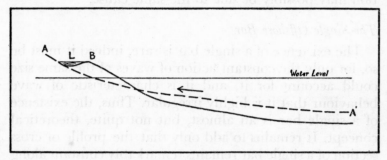

Fig. V.1.—The 'swash' bar.

have no great height. Thus, should a storm follow it will be combed back into the sea in a matter of minutes to form what has been described as a winter profile.

It is doubtful whether the swash bar exists permanently in nature, and it is necessary to look elsewhere for an explanation of the barrier bars and beaches which present such a difficult problem.[1]

THE OFFSHORE BAR

The processes which form the offshore bar have been described in Chapter III, p. 60. It is to be clearly understood that a single constant wave train in a tideless sea *must* form an offshore bar. A change in wave height has the effect of moving a bar previously formed (or of destroying a first and building a second), and the effect of tidal rise and fall is to move the bar-forming processes

[1] Since writing this Miss E. D. Andrew has kindly allowed me to read her unpublished account of what is undoubtedly an ephemeral swash bar at Porthmissen Beach, Cornwall.

up or down the beach so that they operate at no place for so long a time as to produce any obvious result. The offshore bar is to be found almost everywhere in the Mediterranean, but nowhere round the coasts of Britain, though, as will be seen later, the runnel and bar formation may possibly be due to the same cause.

The Single Offshore Bar

The existence of a single bar is rare, indeed it must be so, for only the constant action of waves of the same size could account for it, and it is characteristic of wave behaviour that it is highly irregular. Thus, the existence of a single bar is an almost, but not quite, theoretical concept. It remains to add only that the profile or cross section of a single bar remains remarkably constant along its length. This is due to the effect of the longshore movement of water. It will be readily understood how a slight

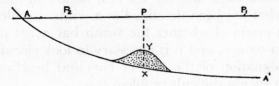

FIG. V.2.—Bar height to water depth ratio of offshore bar.

movement in the direction of the bar crest where the sand is moving freely during storms, will tend to remove irregularities so leaving a smooth ridge.

Dr. King, having examined a large number of bar profiles, has pointed out an interesting relation between the height of the bar above the barless profile. In Fig. V.2 if AA′ represents a barless profile on which the bar is superimposed, there is a relation, $XY = \frac{1}{2} PY$. This relation, which was pointed out by Dr. King in 1946, would have been of great interest during the war while planning landing operations for assault units. It was most important then to know the depths of water on the crests of bars.

As has been explained on p. 60, bars form under the plunge line of the waves. In Fig. V.2 P is the plunge point; if the waves were to be increased in height so that they began to break at P_1 a bar would begin to form under that point, and the bar at P would be gradually pulled back by the destructive waves under the surf towards P_1. If, on the other hand, the wave height were reduced so that the plunge point occurred at P_2, a bar would begin to form under P_2, and the bar under P would tend to move towards it. But this movement might be slow, because the smaller waves would have relatively little energy. A large change in wave height which had the effect of moving the plunge point from P_2 to P_1 on the other hand, besides forming a bar at P_1 in the manner described above, would almost certainly bring about the rapid destruction of a bar in the very shoal water at P_2 because it would then be in the surf zone.

Double Offshore Bars (see Plate IV)

Fig. V.3 is characteristic of the kind of beach profile that has been observed on the open beaches of the Mediterranean such as the North Coast of Africa, the West Coast of Italy or the South Coast of France, and which is commonly found on tideless beaches. Of the two bars the outer is formed and governed by the storm waves which occur. Repeated surveys have shown that this bar varies little in height, and its horizontal movement is very slow. The inner, or smaller bar, reacts to the small fair weather waves which having little energy have little effect on the large outer bar. These waves, though small, suffer frequent and rapid changes in size; a change of wave height from one foot to two feet could take place in a few minutes during a freshening wind and the contrary effect need not take much longer.

In such circumstances it is fascinating to follow the change in the small inner bar. This must surely be one of the most satisfactory demonstrations of beach change that we are able to observe. Fig. V.3 shows the changes that occurred on a beach with double bars at intervals of roughly one year. During a subsequent storm the inner bar was completely destroyed, while the outer bar suffered little change. This profile is typical of many beaches in the Mediterranean.

Multiple Bars

It not infrequently happens in tideless seas that there are more than two bars; in the Adriatic for instance there are often four, especially on the sandy beaches of Albania. The explanation would appear to be that the incidence of winds is such that four distinct wave heights occur frequently and that other heights are of relatively rare occurrence. Thus each of these wave systems with its own plunge line is responsible for forming one of the bars. As far as is known this explanation has not been satisfactorily established, but the existence of a bar at a given level on a beach *must* be due to the action of waves of the appropriate size for an appreciable length of time. Reference to this is made on p. 115 in a discussion of the runnel and bar formation on tidal beaches.

Crescentic Bars (see Plate IV)

Air photographs have revealed the existence of bars which consist of a number of crescents. They exist as single or double series; a beach with a double row of such bars would appear to a bather to be very uneven. This formation is never seen on long straight beaches, but is characteristic of small embayed beaches lying between headlands. This is readily understood, for such an irregular sea bed, if it could be produced on a long open beach, would soon be reduced to the continuous bar

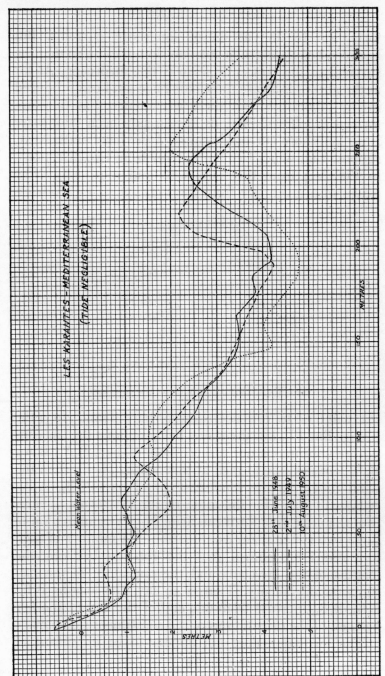

FIG. V.3.—Offshore bars; double series.

formation by the action of longshore currents. But between headlands such currents do not exist, so that the survival of the crescentic form is not surprising. As far as the author is aware these bars have not been produced in the laboratory, but there is evidence that they are formed as follows. First, as has already been said, there is no longshore current because of the headlands. Next, suppose that winds frequently blow from two directions; in Fig. V.4 from the south-west and south-east. Now waves of a given size from the south-west, in a tideless

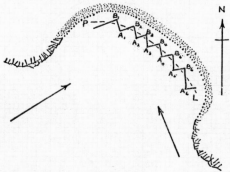

FIG. V.4.—Formation of crescentic sandbars.

sea, will tend to form accretions or bars of sand along the plunge line PL, but the waves being oblique the bar cannot be continuous but a succession of bars B_1A_1, B_2A_2, B_3A_3, etc., will be formed at this depth. Then, when the wind moves to the south-east small bars A_1B_2, A_2B_3, A_3B_4, will result for the same reason. It seems obvious that the crescentic form can arise from a combination of these two systems. An examination of a number of such formations has shown that the relation between the lengths of the crescents and the curvature of the bay supports this theory. That is to say, the lengths B_1B_2, B_2B_3, B_3B_4, increase from one end of the bay to another because of the orientations of the constituent side bars.

The formation does not appear to be important at

normal times; such beaches were very unfavourable for amphibious operations during the war of 1939–45. There is no reason to suppose that they are in any way associated with beach cusps; all the evidence is that they are not.

The Runnel and Bar Formation (see Plate III)

This formation, which Johnson calls the 'Low and Ball', occurs on tidal beaches. Fig. V.5 shows a typical example. It is common in the English Channel, on the Lancashire coast and on the West Coast of Malaya; doubtless it exists in many parts of the world. As far as is known it does not occur on beaches exposed to a large fetch, which indicates that it cannot exist if the beach is subject to the action of very large waves. Detailed daily observations at Blackpool over a period of two years have shown that the banks change slowly in size, shape and position. As is to be expected the lowest bar changes more rapidly than those further up the beaches, being most frequently subject to wave action. The runnels are often deepened when the beach is uncovered because, as the tide recedes, they form part of the drainage pattern of the beach; sometimes considerable quantities of water can be seen flowing along the runnels, and there are periodic breaks through the bars where these streams cross from a higher runnel to a lower. The scouring of the drainage streams sometimes causes the runnels to become abnormally deep and steepsided.

While it must be said that their formation is not clearly understood, the fact that there are usually four bars suggests that we have four repetitions of the offshore bar (see p. 110) on a tidal beach. If we can rule out the possibility of waves so great that minor bars become obliterated it seems that their formation can be explained as follows.

During a lunar month the sea level will have 'stood'

or been near the four levels of high and low springs and high and low neaps for much longer periods than at any other level. During such stands of the tide the waves might have time to form an offshore bar, which could well explain the frequent occurrence of four bars. The number might be increased if a double or multiple bar were formed at low springs.

Fig. V.5 shows a profile of a beach south of Blackpool. It was surveyed daily for more than a year during the war of 1939–45 in order to ascertain the rate of change of the beach because it is very similar in many ways to the Normandy beaches. This profile has been selected at random, and the relation between the bars and the levels of high and low springs and neaps may not appear very convincing. In the absence of any other explanation of the features, however, this seems to be the most rewarding line of investigation to pursue. Continuous records of wave systems would probably provide a clue to their part, if any, in bar formation.

Although there is no evidence that these runnels and bars exist on beaches fringing great oceans where very large waves occur, their occurrence is probably much more common than has been suspected. They are very clearly seen on aerial photographs, and they have often been seen on photographs of beaches where observers on the ground had failed to see them. Air photographs of many beaches on our south coast show bars and runnels, the bars appearing as dry sand, and the runnels wet. Some of these have been surveyed, and the amplitude between bar crest and the trough of the runnel was less than six inches. Inspection on the ground had not detected them.

Shoreline Curves

In plan, the form of beaches, whether of sand or shingle, is usually a smooth curve, concave to the sea.

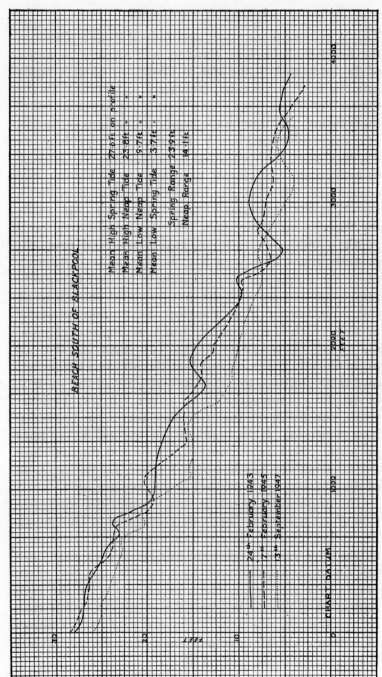

FIG. V.5.—Profiles of a runnel and bar beach formation.

This is evident from maps, and indeed from a glance at the beaches themselves. Readers will already be aware of the formation of the spit at Chesil; or of such sandy beaches as Woolacombe, Newquay, or Rhossili in the Gower Peninsula. There have been many explanations of these forms, and these have been summarized by Lewis. It is discernible on Plate V, but the examples there are not good ones. It appears that the authorities who attempt to explain this curvilinear form tend to divide into two camps, one advocating a longshore current hypothesis, the other the dominant breaker hypothesis. Put briefly the theories are these; first, that the longshore currents gently mould the coastline, taking material from the protuberances, and using it to fill the pockets. Alternatively the supporters of the dominant breaker hypothesis argue that the currents are not powerful enough to do this, and that it must therefore be a more powerful agency which is responsible, and that breakers can and do provide the necessary energy. It is surprising that the arguments do not point out that the breakers themselves owe their positions to the nature or form of the sea bed, or to the circumstance that a sea current, however small, can transport material once waves have raised it into suspension. If the breakers are responsible, we must go further back in our investigations and discover how the adjacent sea bed has been formed, for the positions of the breakers are governed by its configuration.

The importance of taking into account the configuration of the sea bed is clearly demonstrated at Dungeness. Steers [1], p. 326. Here the orientations of the shingle ridges have varied from time to time as they have been put down in orientations which vary by 90°, and these alignments are clearly determined more by the configuration of the sea bed and the existing coastline than by the fetch of the sea. There are excellent examples of similar local and radical changes in the orientation of comparable ridges on the Albanian coast; see Plate VI.

As is so often the case, both parties are right in part, but each must make some concession to the other. Surely the one factor which above all others decides the orientation of the Chesil Spit is the fact that it is anchored to the mainland near Abbotsbury at its northern end, and to the Isle of Portland in the south; this being so, its *general* direction is fore-ordained. This consideration applies to all beaches which lie between rocky headlands. (Shore-lines near 'loose' headlands such as Dungeness will be dealt with later.) The effect of breakers, or waves, and longshore drift is to define the nature of the coastal curve between the headlands. The dissipation of wave energy between headlands (see p. 68) is relevant to this process, but in outline what happens appears to be this:

Wave action gets the beach material into suspension. There will be little material for disposal on the head-lands, because it has been previously removed. In the pockets of sand or shingle in the bays the amount of material in suspension at a given time and place will be a function of turbulence; that is to say, of the closeness of the area to the plunge point of the waves running. This in turn depends upon the *depth* of the water.

If the sea bed is very uneven, the coastline will be un-even; this must be so, irrespective of the direction from which the waves are coming. But, while the material is in suspension, a longshore water movement will to some extent smooth out any unevenness in the sea bed. Tur-bulence will be relatively great on the shoals, and the current will carry the material thence and will drop it in the deeper places where the turbulence is less. And a con-sequence of this smoothing of the sea bed will be that the waves themselves will become more regular; the plunge line will assume a more regular form, and in due course the water line will become bow-shaped in form, the offending protuberances within the bay having been removed. That the curve of the beach should be concave is explained in pp. 68 et seq. Indeed a little thought will show that this process, considered along with the effect of longshore currents, which is considerable, is sufficient to explain the form of shoreline curves.

Spits and Bars

Spits are frequently encountered on coastlines the world over; they exist in a wide variety of forms, and may consist of sand or shingle, or both. Round our own coastline Chesil Beach is well known, as are the bars at Barmouth and Aberdovey, or the shingle bank known as Orfordness. On the Continent are more impressive examples, such as the ridges lying between the lagoons in the Sète region of France or the Nehrungen which enclose the haffs in the Baltic. In America are innumerable examples to which Johnson makes ample reference; some of them are features of considerable magnitude, such as the barrier beaches in the Caribbean, Florida Keys and Sandy Hook Bay. In fact, little is known about the formation of many bars; relatively few of them have been examined by borings, and until this has been done it would be imprudent to be dogmatic about their methods of construction. If we now are any nearer than our predecessors to knowing how they have been formed it is only because by a process of elimination we are in some cases able to say how they were *not* formed.

One kind of spit is simply explained. Lines of coral reefs on an emergent coastline clearly provide a platform on which subsequent action by waves and currents can build spits or barrier islands.

Spits are important for their own sakes, for they are often quite large; but they are also important because they are the enclosing feature of lagoons and haffs. Just as their forms vary, and the materials of which they are formed may differ widely, so their origins will differ. There is no space here to examine the problem in great detail, but sufficient spits will be described to explain the probable construction of a few, and to illustrate the complexity and obscurity of others.

Johnson appears to accept Gilbert's theory that, on a coast of emergence, the offshore bar will rise relative to the water until it emerges from it and exists as a 'land' feature, that is to say it is permanently above sea level. This theory might account for some shingle features, but it most emphatically cannot explain bars of sand which are high and dry, and most of the offshore bars which have been studied in detail consist, superficially at least, of sand. As has been explained on p. 110, the position of offshore bars in the first place depends entirely upon the plunge line of waves. The bars are moved up and down the beach as the position of the plunge line changes and this position might vary horizontally over scores of feet in a matter of a few hours. If the bar approached the water edge, the first violent storm would destroy it. Thus it is indefensible to argue that a feature which can move so rapidly can remain in being during the time required for a vertical land movement of many feet—which could not take place in less than several centuries. It is also to be observed that offshore bars decrease in size as they approach the waterline; the author is not aware of a single instance of the survival of a large offshore bar near water level.

The same argument applies to the suggestion that these bars originate from the *swash* bar (see p. 109) if the bar consists of sand. Such features, when formed, are too small to survive the violence of succeeding storms; they cannot possibly be the genesis of large permanent coastal features.

How then can these very considerable features be formed if they do not rest on coral platforms? The question is best answered by examining them one by one, and by using the evidence of their substance, dimensions, positions—including orientation—and the fetch of the sea, wave patterns, etc., to deduce the formative processes which are most likely to be responsible. But before doing this there are three factors which appear capable of making important contributions to the genesis and growth of spits. Beaches of *shingle* differ from those of sand in that they do lend themselves to the formation of ridges above water level. As has been explained on p. 65, it is characteristic of wave action on shingle that in certain circumstances particles should be thrown above the water line. Chesil Beach is an example of this. Secondly, once such a ridge has been thrown up, if there is any sand in the vicinity, the shingle will make an excellent trap for it, and indeed given an adequate base of shingle, and a sufficient movement of sand, a feature which at first sight appears to consist of sand may be formed. Thirdly, bearing in mind these two processes, a bar may be formed if a feature such as C (see Fig. V.6) is being eroded by wave action when there is a drift in a coastwise direction, say AB. In such circumstances the eroded material will be moved by the current, and will

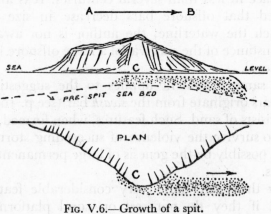

FIG. V.6.—Growth of a spit.

be carried along in the manner in which a rubbish tip grows. The cliff is broken down, and the fragments are carried in a direction AB, forming a ridge. Being shingle, the level can be maintained above water by processes already described. The rate of growth will depend upon the rate of erosion, and in consequence upon the amount of material available, and also the depth of water in which it is being deposited, and thus the height and volume of the bank.

Bearing in mind then these general considerations as to how bars or spits can, and cannot be formed, let us see whether it is possible to explain a few well-known features.

Chesil Beach

This remarkable bank of shingle, nine miles long between its roots at Abbotsbury in the north-west and Portland Isle in the south-east, has for some time attracted the attention of geologists, geographers and oceanographers. In places the ridge rises 43 feet above the level of high springs, and its average width is nearly 200 yards. The shingle foreshore continues further to the north-west in great quantities, but it is the pensinsular ridge, backed by the Fleet, which is of particular interest.

It is interesting, and in some ways gratifying, that there is so much speculation about a feature which is so well known and which has been studied for so long. But even today the authorities ask such questions as, 'Where does the constituent material come from?' 'Why does it not disappear by wastage?' 'Why does it not move?' and, 'In which directions are the shingle fragments travelling?' Let us dispose of the second and third of these two questions by stating at once that the whole feature *is* shrinking. There is no evidence that new material is being fed into it from outside sources, and, this being so, the whole bank must shrink as each of its constituent pebbles is abraded by wave action. As to movement, the evidence

of maps is that between surveys of 1880 and 1928 the
bank was driven in some places as much as 90 feet to
the north-east. This, too, is what one would expect. On
the reasonable assumption that the seaward face tends in
the long run to preserve the same shape, remembering,
too, that during very heavy storms stones are thrown on
to and over the ridge by waves which can in no circumstances recover them, there *must* be a movement away
from the sea.

The first and fourth questions are not so easily dis-
posed of. In a way they are closely interrelated. The
shingle consists mainly of flints, the largest being at
the south-east end. This is consistent with the fact that
while the east-going and west-going currents are almost
balanced, there is a *slight* predominance of west-going
streams. But while this could explain why the pebbles at
the north-west extremity are smaller, having travelled
furthest, it does not explain why the large flints at the
south-east end have not been removed, since there seems
to be no new supply of them from Portland Island. Nor
does it explain why, at the north-west end of the beach
there are pebbles differing from the flints at the south-
east end, but which are of the same material as rocks
found at present only to the west of Lyme Regis. There
appears to be no hydraulic process which could bring
pebbles to Chesil from a point so far to the west.

Arkell points out that there need not necessarily be a
close correlation between beach shingles and the present
geology, since the shingle could have been derived from
formations which have now disappeared. Indeed it
seems that one must frequently accept this explanation
for coastal features. Shingle exists in the sea bed off
Chesil Beach in large quantities; all of it, as far as is
known, is flint.

Assuming, then, the existence of a large quantity of
shingle in the vicinity, the existence and general form

Long-crested waves advancing upon, and being retarded by, the shelving beach in St. Aubyn's Bay, Jersey

PLATE VI

Upper: Underwater feature between island and mainland.

Lower: Successive depositions on an Albanian beach, showing former shorelines now well inland

of Chesil Beach are easy to understand. By methods already discussed in the chapter on processes, the stones will be thrown into an embankment; wave action will get them into suspension, and the waves and currents whose movements are closely governed by the configuration of the sea bed will account for the curvilinear form of the beach, anchored as it is to the mainland at Abbotsbury and to Portland Isle.

It is interesting to speculate upon the future of this bank; it is being slowly driven towards the mainland, and as it wastes and shrinks it will be more frequently overtopped by storm waves. Chesil bank appears to have reached a critical stage in its life.

Simple Spits

Reference has already been made to the kind of spit which is formed by the coastwise transport of material by wave and current action. Features which are the result of this process are very common in Ceylon, where during the dry spells in the monsoon climate bars form at the mouths of rivers.

As the river flow diminishes sand is carried across the mouth until in many cases a bar forms, and the river mouth is sealed until the next rains cause the river to flood. The rate of transport of this sand can be quite remarkable. A glance at the one-inch maps will show that the mouths of many rivers in Ceylon have been considerably deflected presumably by repetitions of this process. It seems probable that the bar is initially a swash bar; thus the lateral movement is caused by coastwise drifting, and the movement in a direction normal to the coastline by wave action.

The Nehrungen

Features which appear to owe their origins to this kind of process are to be found in the south-east of the

Baltic, though here the swash bar effect must be ruled out. Their nomenclature on maps is perhaps confusing since they have at different times been given names by the Poles and the Germans; but the three features to be

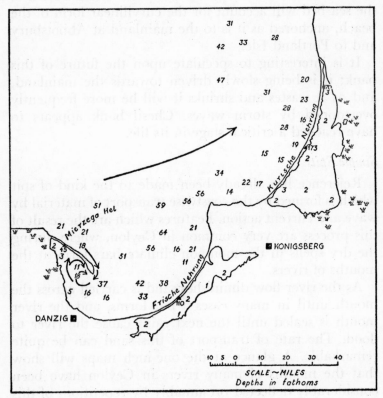

FIG. V.7.—Spits in S.E. Baltic.

considered are described on the International I/M map as Mierzega Hel, Frische Nehrung, and Kurische Nehrung. As is indicated in Fig. V.7 they are banks of considerable size, the last mentioned being over 70 miles long, in places 170 feet high, and up to two miles in width.

126

The middle and eastern spits have, save for channels which allow egress of river water from the interior, completely sealed off lagoons or haffs on their landward sides, but the most westerly spit forms a pensinsula only about half as long as the other two. The two haffs are shallow, the deepest soundings inside them being only three fathoms, while Mierzega Hel has deeper water inside it, one sounding showing eighteen fathoms. Charted soundings, some of which are shown in Fig. V.7, suggest that they were all built in similar depths, for the submarine slopes are very similar to the seaward of all three. All are 'rooted' in, or have grown from the west, and this is consistent with the Baltic current in this area, which is east-going, and with the transport which one would expect from waves which are predominantly generated by winds from the west. There is a large amount of glacial material on the coast, and the recent tendency has been for the coastline to emerge.

There can be little doubt that these spits have been formed by the transport by wave and current action of material which was eroded from their western extremities. Probably they existed for some time as shingle features, with an admixture of sand, but, once they were well above the level of destructive action of waves they were able to trap and hold some of the considerable amount of sand that was being blown about. Thus, these peninsulas, which appear as features of sand, and which indeed are largely composed of sand, owe their origins to the availability of shingle on which the sand could be deposited. This shingle has been progressively moved as a kind of embankment which has grown eastward from its source of material.

The Frische and Kurische Nehrungen now form arcs which lie smoothly between their points of origin and their eastern extremities; they may not have grown in this direction in the first place, but, once they had reached their eastern limits, the action of the sea moulded them to their present forms. It is interesting to speculate upon the ultimate form of the Mierzega Hel if it continues to grow to the eastward. The disparity between the depths inside the Mierzega Hel and the other two is almost certainly explained by sedimentation which has taken place very rapidly inside the eastern lagoons since they were enclosed. There are indications that silting is taking place inside the Mierzega Hel at the North-western end where the sea currents now have little effect.

One is led to wonder why the Mierzega Hel has not, like the other two spits, completed its growth until it joined the land again at its eastern extremity. All appear to have been formed in about ten or twenty fathoms of water, and all seem to have been formed by similar processes. There can, among many possibilities, be two main causes. The first that the material at the root of Mierzega Hel is not available in sufficient quantities, the second, that the marine forces are not so powerful. Certainly the aspect of the westernmost spit appears to indicate that neither current nor waves would be as effective as on the other two; and this is probably the explanation. It is held by some authorities that there was an island at Hel at the south-east of the peninsula before it was completed and that the spit built up to this; indeed its shape is said to be that of a club which is the literal meaning of 'Mierzega'. The existence of an island could also contribute to the limitation in the length of the peninsula, especially in view of the pattern of the currents shown on Fig. V.7.

The process described above, usually in association with the emergence of the coastline, probably explains how most of the large spits and banks have been formed. There are many such features in the Gulf of Mexico, and on the Eastern Coast of North America. Nearer home the

Étangs in the South of France, Thau near Sète and Sigean near Narbonne appear to owe their origins to the same causes as the Nehrungen in the Baltic; the bars are not so high, and the amount of sand available appears to be less. It would be unwise to postulate theories about Thau and Sigean, however, without first studying the many lagoons, the largest of them being the Étang de Vaccares in the Rhône delta. Here there is a plentiful supply of material for the formation of a spit, and the evolution of a lagoon within the delta area is not difficult to understand. Wave action would raise a shingle bank and the coast-wise currents are capable of providing the necessary coastwise drifting.

The detritus brought down by the Rhône would be ample for the formation of all the spits in the Golfe du Lion; but if this is the source we must assume a west-going drift, while the present evidence is that it is in fact east-going, and it does not seem possible it could have been different since the last ice age.

At present no satisfactory explanation of these bars has been put forward. Borings might indicate the source of the materials and the date of the lagoons, but until such evidence is available we can only speculate as to their origins.

Orfordness is a shingle feature caused by the transport of shingle by current and wave action in a way that has already been described. If there were sufficient sand in the vicinity the ridge might well become a kind of minia-ture Nehrung. The interesting feature here, however, is not so much the shingle spit as the headland, or the 'Ness', 'Neb', or 'Nose', midway between Aldeburgh and the southern extremity of the shingle bank. This kind of feature is discussed elsewhere under 'headlands' (see p. 133 et seq.).

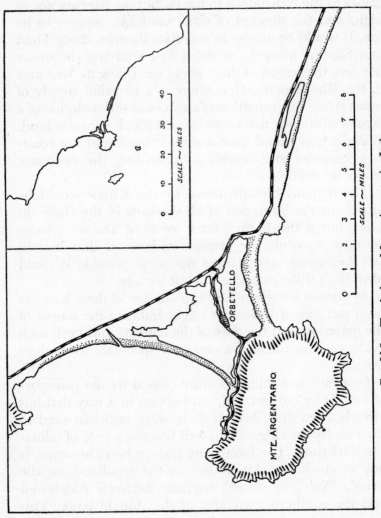

Fig. V.8.—Tombolos at Monte Argentario, Italy.

Tombolos

This name has been given by earlier writers to the interesting, but comparatively unimportant feature consisting of a bar connecting an island to the mainland. The form usually associated with it is shown in Fig. V.8,

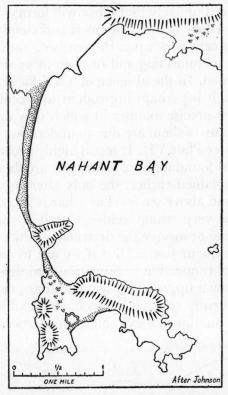

FIG. V.9.—Spit, or tombolo at Nahant, Mass., U.S.A.

that is to say, there are two connecting bars. Johnson uses the name for a single connecting bar, see Fig. V.9. While the bars, looked at one at a time, may appear similar, there seems little reason to ascribe a special name to the features shown in Fig. V.8 for it appears to be a simple connecting bar, similar to Chesil or the

Mierzega Hel. The formation of bars connecting islands to the mainland does merit a brief discussion, if only to consider why they sometimes exist, whereas elsewhere, in circumstances which at first sight seem comparable, they do not.

If the water between an island and the mainland is deep, it is most unlikely that a bar will form; alternatively, if the sea bed between them is sufficiently shallow, wave action can work upon the sea bed, and, with current action, a connecting spit or even more simply, *spits* may be formed. In the absence of a satisfactory study of the features, it is perhaps imprudent to speculate in detail upon the precise manner in which they are formed; probably many of them are due to underlying geological formations (see Plate VI). It seems highly probable, however, that the foundations of other spits are shingle, for as has been explained earlier, the only alternative method of raising sand above sea level as a bar is as a swash bar, and there is very strong evidence that if these are of sand they cannot survive the destructive action by waves during subsequent storms. But if we are to assume that some kind of connection between the mainland and the island is thrown up, whether as swash bars, or as shingle bars subsequently covered by sand, the double tombolo seems to be an almost inevitable consequence.

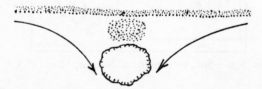

FIG. V.10.—Possible method of formation of tombolos.

In Fig. V.10 suppose that there is a shoal between the island and the mainland; suppose, further, that there is, along this coastline, a to and fro current due to tides or to fluctuations of the wind. These currents will be deflected by the island and the shoal, and wave action will be refracted to cause transport of material in the directions shown by the arrows in Fig. V.10. The formation of the two spits thus follows as a matter of course.

A classical example of this kind of feature is found at Monte Argentario in Italy, and is shown in Fig. V.8. It will be seen that the island, being situated at an angle in the coastline, invites the action of currents and waves from its two sides even more than if it were situated off a straight coastline. The presence of enough shingle to raise a ridge at the back of the beach would suffice to ensure the formation of the double spit.

Headlands

On p. 68 it was explained that promontories are more vulnerable to wave attack than bays because of the concentration of energy upon the headlands, and the dissipation of it in the bays. So far we have assumed that the survival of headlands is due to their hardness; that the prominent parts of the coastline are resistant and the intervening bays soft by comparison. This indeed does explain why such features as Worm's Head, Beachy Head, and Cap Grisnez still stand. It is at first sight therefore surprising to observe that there are some features which on a map appear to be equally prominent which consist not of hard consolidated rock, but often of loose shingle, and sometimes even of sand. Some examples of such features are, Dungeness, Orfordness, Selsey Bill and the Ness at Benacre, a few miles south of Lowestoft. This last example is mentioned because it has probably been studied more systematically than any other headlands in this country, and because its behaviour seems typical of headlands in general. Dungeness consists of shingle ridges which, as they have formed and moved, have enclosed or covered the original marsh hinterland; Orfordness consists of loose beach shingle, while Selsey Bill is composed of the Brackle-sham beds which are chiefly loose sandy material partly of estuarine origin, and partly marine. What is surprising about salients of such soft material is that they survive; for if it is true that headlands are subject to a more severe battering by wave action than bays or even straight coastlines, they should have been destroyed long ago. Why then are they not broken down until the coastline is straight?

It can be assumed that shingle is well able to take punishment from waves. The particles may be thrown about; they may be chipped or broken, but on the whole, shingle as a substance is little affected by wave action, unlike cliffs which, once broken down, cannot be re-formed. On the other hand, shingle is very mobile; it can be moved by waves and currents at a really remarkable speed. What we have to explain, therefore, is why the shingle at these headlands which is often moved about, and probably at times removed from the headland, tends to be put back again. Let us look for the forces which can account for such a remarkable replacement.

It has already been stated that the direct onset of wave attack by itself would tend to destroy a headland; thus it would appear that the forces which form headlands must be forces acting laterally along the coast; furthermore, the forces operating on each side of the headland must be very nearly balanced, or it would be moved to one side or the other under the influence of the predominant lateral force.

Table III opposite is a general analysis of the currents on each of the four headlands that have been selected for attention. The figures given represent the mean current in knots at the times stated, that is to say, it is the mean between the spring and neap velocities given in the *Admiralty Atlas of Tidal Streams*. The figures are necessarily approximate because the scale of the atlas is such

134

that they cannot be given in very great detail; further the velocities shown are usually for distances of a mile or two offshore and these must be higher than the rate of movement inshore where turbulence is greatest and where the greatest amount of material is in motion. The tables are, however, useful in that they demonstrate that at each of our four headlands the water movement on its two sides is fairly evenly balanced.

Time Relative to High Water DOVER	SELSEY Going to		DUNGENESS Going to		ORFORDNESS Going to		BENACRE or COVEHITHE NESS Going to	
	W	E	W	E	N	S	N	S
	Movement in knots							
6 hours before		0·5	1·2			0·4		0·1
5 ,, ,,		1·7	1·6			0·4		1·4
4 ,, ,,		1·2	2·0			1·5		2·1
3 ,, ,,		1·0	0·7			2·0		2·0
2 ,, ,,		0·7		0·7		2·0		2·0
1 ,, ,,	0·1			0·6		0·7		0·7
High Water	1·6			0·7		0·2		0·2
1 hour after	2·0			0·6	0·6		0·7	
2 ,, ,,	1·6			1·3	1·7		1·7	
3 ,, ,,	1·0			0·9	2·0		2·0	
4 ,, ,,	0·6			0·3	1·7		1·7	
5 ,, ,,		0·3	0·3		1·5		1·5	
6 ,, ,,		0·5	1·0		0·2		0·2	
Totals Approximate movement per tide in sea miles.	6·9	5·9	6·8	5·1	7·7	7·2	7·8	8·5

TABLE III.

Thus there is evidence that the *current* movement on the two sides of the headlands considered is very nearly balanced. This is obviously a matter of some importance, but it matters less than the balance between the action of the waves on each side of the headlands. For this no statistics exist but we are forced to the conclusion that the balance must exist. Observations made at Covehithe suggest something near equality; it is reasonable to suppose that it is so at Orfordness and Selsey, but at a first glance one would expect Dungeness to be affected more by south-westerlies than by seas from the east. In the absence of precise observations we are bound to the conclusion that this is not so to any great extent, although the fact that in historical times the Ness has moved to the eastward is almost certainly due to the push that is exerted by waves from the south-west. It may well be that if the total effect of waves provides transport to the east the total current effect inshore is in the opposite direction. The above table does in fact show that the west-going stream predominates.

Steers [1] deals at length with the literature on Dungeness, and those interested are advised to read his account. Suffice to say here that a large mass of shingle which almost certainly came from the west, having been thrown into a complex system of ridges, now owes its survival as a headland to a kind of moulding or stroking movement on both sides which transports the material towards the point of the Ness. It is the action, by both currents and waves, which must explain the formation and survival of every headland of soft material.

At Selsey the same process goes on. Orfordness differs only in that the forces on the two sides being imperfectly balanced, the Ness, and the shingle spit to the south spit, have moved to the southward. The summary of current velocities in Table III suggests that the north-going current is greater than the south-going. It has already been pointed out that the current inshore may not follow the trends a mile or two to seaward, but even if it were true the predominance of waves from the north over those from the south could account for the southward trend where the current behaviour is so evenly balanced. It is to be noted that the fetch in a south-east direction is a little less than that at Benacre Ness. It has been suggested that the southward travel of shingle on the spit, especially to the south of the Ness, is assisted by the flow in the river. As far as is known this view is not supported by observations, and at first sight it would appear that the part played by the river is small.

The coastline at Covehithe and Kessingland in Suffolk has now been systematically surveyed for nine years. Surveys were made in the first instance because it appeared that erosion and deposition were taking place at points within a mile or so of one another.

Fig. V.11 shows what in fact is taking place. On a coastline which is in general being eroded, there appears to be deposition on the northward side of Benacre Ness. This process seems to have been going on for a long time; the pecked line shows Saxton's plotting of it on his map of 1575. It is very doubtful whether the Ness was in fact as large as Saxton has shown it; probably he was influenced in drawing his map by the perspectives seen from points of view to the north and south of it. There is no reason however to question the position of it, especially in view of the evidence of subsequent surveys. Fig. V.11 shows the positions of the point of the Ness at various times, and these show that it has moved steadily towards the north, a trend which continues and is apparent from surveys made periodically since 1948. The Ness consists of sand and shingle, the proportions varying very widely from place to place, but the point of the Ness consists entirely of shingle.

In the past it has been assumed that shore features move with the current, and in this particular part of the coast the spit at Orfordness and the mouth of the Yare at Great Yarmouth are examples which support this view. Yet, midway between these two features is a headland which moves steadily against the current. It is necessary to repeat the caution that has been given earlier that there are difficulties in assessing the precise nature of current flow; the available observations are too meagre, and in any case they do not exist for shallow water. According to the *Atlas of Tides and Tidal Streams, British Islands and Adjacent Waters*, at Smith's Knoll, 52° 43′ N. and 2° 17′ E., the 'residual current is 2·6 sea miles per lunar day in a direction 135°. The same document indicates a southward trend over the whole of the neighbouring coastline, though it is to be expected that the movement on the beach would be less than in the open sea. Williams [2] found that current measurements made close inshore varied very erratically; they did not point to the same conclusion, but they were not made over sufficiently long periods to be accepted as evidence to the contrary. Such observations as were made demonstrated very clearly that the coastwise movement of water—and therefore material—inshore is determined more by wind and waves than by the general circulation in the deeper water to seaward, whether this be due to oceanic currents or tidal streams. There were many occasions when the movement on the beach was not in the same sense as that published for Smith's Knoll.

The northern face of Benacre Ness is so orientated that it halts and in part retains material which is moving southward as a result of current movement and wave action. On the neighbouring coastline erosion proceeds unchecked; only on this northern face of the Ness is material held, with the result that while most of the coastline is receding, this short section is growing to seaward, with the effect that the Ness appears to travel northward. The rate of this northward movement must be decreasing because the amount of material available for transport is steadily diminishing. If we assume that nothing travels southward past Lowestoft, the Ness in

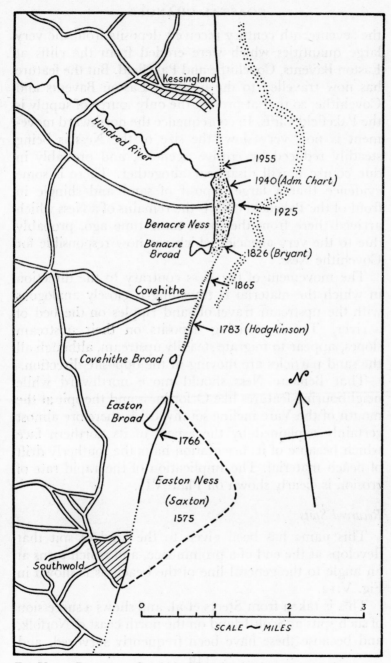

Kessingland

Hundred River

1955

1940 (Adm. Chart)

1925

Benacre Ness

Benacre Broad

1826 (Bryant)

1865

Covehithe

1783 (Hodgkinson)

Covehithe Broad

Easton Broad

1766

Easton Ness (Saxton) 1575

Southwold

N

0   1   2   3

SCALE ~ MILES

Fig. V.11.—Benacre, or Covehithe Ness, showing its movement since 1575.

the seventeenth century received deposits from the very large quantities which were eroded from the cliffs at Easton Bavents, Covehithe and Pakefield. But the feature has now travelled to the north of Easton Bavents and Covehithe, so that at present the only source of supply is the Pakefield Cliffs. In consequence the northward movement is now very slow; the size of the Ness is being steadily reduced by erosive agencies, and probably in due course it will disappear altogether. There is some evidence that a large deposit of sand and shingle in front of the Pakefield cliffs is the remains of a Ness which arrived there from the south some time ago, probably due to the very agencies which are now responsible for Covehithe Ness.

The movement of the Ness contrary to the direction in which the material is travelling is closely analogous with the upstream travel of sand ripples on the bed of a river. These, receiving deposits on their upstream slopes, appear to migrate steadily upstream, although all the sand particles are moving in the opposite direction.

That Benacre Ness should move northward while neighbouring features like Orfordness and the spit at the mouth of the Yare incline southward is therefore almost certainly explained by the aspect of its northern face which because of its orientation halts the southerly drift of beach material. The implication of the rapid rate of erosion is clearly shown on Plate VII.

Recurved Spits

This name has been given to the kind of spit that develops at the end of a prominence, and which turns at an angle to the general line of the beach as is shown in Fig. V.12.

This is taken from Steers et al. and shows a succession of such spits at Scolt Island on the north coast of Norfolk, and because these have been frequently surveyed, and

Plate VII

Dunwich Church 1904 and 1914. The church finally disappeared from the cliff top with a fall in 1919

Plate VIII

A sea wall damaged by wave action

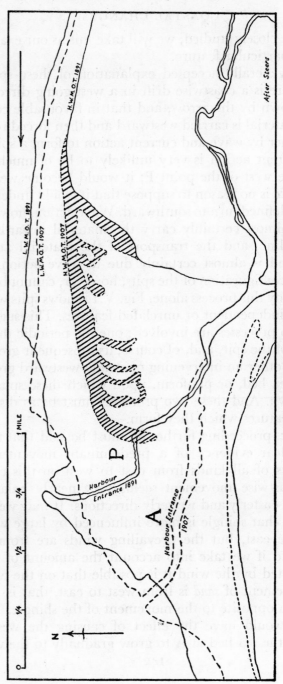

FIG. V.12.—Recurved Spits at Scolt Island, Norfolk.

L

the area closely studied, we will take this as our example of this particular feature.

The generally accepted explanation of these spits is that there is a coastwise drift in a west-going direction, as is shown by the arrow, and that in favourable conditions material is carried westward and then forced round the corner by wave and current action to form a spit. In fact current action is very unlikely to be of much importance west of the point P; it would become weaker, and there is no reason to suppose that it would undergo a clearly defined turn to southward. Wave action, however, would almost certainly carry the material towards the plunge line, and the transport of the material at this distal end is almost certainly due to wave action; the precise configuration of the spits, however, cannot be explained by this process alone. Fig. V.12 shows spits which exist as independent or unrelated features. This suggests that two processes are involved; one the periodic throwing up of the spit, and, of course, its subsequent growth, and the other an intervening or steady westward growth of the sea bed, or platform, upon which these spits are laid down. And these two processes must be as distinct as the features which they form.

Before proceeding further it must be said that there is no clear evidence of a predominant movement of materials of all kinds from east to west on this coast. The coastwise movement seems very nearly balanced between easterly and westerly directions. It may well be the case that shingle is more influenced by large waves from the east, but the prevailing winds are from the west, and if we take into account the amount of sand transported by the wind it is possible that on the whole the movement of *sand* is from west to east, that is, in a direction opposite to the movement of the shingle.

This would have the effect of causing the western slope of the sea bed at A to grow gradually to the westward, for the sea bed would be raised as sand was deposited on it by wind and waves from the west. Thus we have a changing sea bed on which the shingle ridges from the west are deposited.

The origin and behaviour of shingle on the north coast of Norfolk is at present shrouded in mystery: different observers, presumably because they have observed in different conditions, have come to conflicting conclusions. We know, however, that shingle does exist there, and that in varying conditions of sea it may move either eastwards or westwards. For our purposes we can safely assume a supply of shingle on the north coast of Scolt Island, and at times, during storms for instance, a long, powerful swell running from east of north; this would cause a ridge of shingle to move to the westward at a depth governed by the nature of the wave action. The waves would be refracted round the growing sandbank at the western end of the island, and, assuming that the waves continued over a high tide, would leave a ridge at the level at which they were being transported. The curving of the distal end depends upon the configuration of the sandbank; obviously the line of the shingle would follow a contour of the sandbank, and if the bank were higher in the middle that at the sides, as it is most likely to be, the curvature is explained. It now requires a period of calmer weather so that the ridge be not destroyed. Renewed growth of the sandbanks lower down the beach could protect the newly formed bank from succeeding destructive wave action. Waves of an appropriate period and height could then drive the bank up the beach and finally above the level of high tides. It is highly probable that shingle banks are frequently thrown up and that those which have survived owe their existence not so much to the combination of circumstances which have gone to their formation, as to circumstances which developed soon after their formation and which saved them from destruction. At Scolt the flowing of sand from the west appears to be a factor of considerable importance.

It is not claimed that the spits at Scolt are formed in this precise way; many factors might intervene to make the story much more complex than the simple sequence that has been outlined. For instance, it is known that there are times when the western end of Scolt Island is eroded, either by wave action or by scour as water leaves the harbour during ebb tides, so that the growth due to the arrival of sand from the west is by no means steady. Still less can it be argued that other spits must be formed in a similar manner. Many detailed and continuous observations are needed before defensible claims can be made. There can be little doubt, however, that the features are due to the simple processes that have been described in Chapter III. What remains to be discovered is the *order* in which the processes have combined to produce any particular result.

Deltas

Deltas are at least as much riverine as marine features, and they will not be discussed at length here. But they can appear as very considerable features on the coastline.

The existence of a delta means quite simply that the river is presenting more sediments to the sea than the sea can remove. It is evident, too, that deltas are unlikely to be formed on coastlines of submergence, because it would be necessary for the river to fill up the estuary before the delta could appear as a protuberance beyond the coastline.

The river therefore must bring down large quantities of silt; if the silt is coarse it will settle more readily than very fine material. Thus the most favourable marine conditions for the evolution of a delta are, a small tidal range, so that the tidal streams will be small, and coastwise transport is at a minimum; a shallow sea, so that the minimum of filling is to be done, a small amount of transport by wave action, and coarse material. It is not true, as is sometimes said, that deltas form only where there is no tide, for while the rise and fall of spring tides at the mouths of the Nile, Tiber and Mississippi is of the order of a foot or two, the corresponding range at the mouth of the Hwang Ho is 14 feet.

The important consideration is quite simply that the river presents silt to the sea faster than the sea removes it. The subsequent configuration of the delta depends upon this ratio of deposition to transport. The mouths of many rivers in Italy, e.g. the Tiber, have slightly developed deltas because the ratio is small. The ratio appears to be higher in the Nile, while an extreme case of a high ratio appears to exist at the mouth of the Mississippi. This delta which is sometimes for obvious reasons described as a 'crowsfoot' delta is very complex, the distributories with their levées reaching far into the sea. The difference between the Tiber and the Mississippi deltas is in principle very simple. The Tiber brings down a small amount of silt which is and was gently stroked to one side or the other, so that the mouth of the river is a flat Δ. But at the mouth of the Mississippi the volume of silt is so large, and the rise and fall of the river flood levels so great, that enormous levées are formed which grow at great speed; one mouth of the Mississippi is said to grow 250 feet to seaward every year. The marine agencies are inadequate to deal with such enormous quantities of material so that the river continues its course into the sea.

The bifurcation of streams in deltas is not a marine process and is not dealt with here, nor is the vertical arrangement of the deltaic beds, save to remark that they follow the simple rules of sedimentation which have been described on p. 14.

Some Cliff Formations

The formation of cliffs has been dealt with elsewhere. In general the process is simple; but some of our more spectacular and beautiful coastal forms are the highly accidented structures which occur in the geological formations which are strongly jointed. The chalks, limestones and sandstones provide some of the best known examples. To quote a few; in chalk, the vertical cliffs of Dover and the Needles in the Isle of Wight; in the carboniferous limestone the remarkable coastline in the Gower peninsula, including the blowhole on Worms Head; and in the red sandstone the stack known as the Old Man of Hoy in the Orkneys and the magnificent arch, the Needle Eye, near Wick. Nothing could be further from the uniform distribution of coastal sands and muds than the abruptness of these features, yet all owe their formation almost entirely to wave action (see Plate I).

What has happened is simply explained if we realize that these jointed rocks are removed by the waves, not grain by grain, but as it were, block by block, the blocks being rectangular in shape. If we think of the rock face as a wall built of bricks held together by weak mortar, then it is easy to see how the waves might loosen the mortar so that one brick becomes dislodged. This hastens the removal of other bricks and the disintegration of the wall is likely to proceed in horizontal and vertical planes, so that the development of vertical cliff faces, arches, caves and stacks ensues. Clearly such forms cannot occur in unjointed or weakly jointed rocks; here the erosion takes place grain by grain rather than brick by brick so that the eroded face takes more regular forms such as rounded rocks or inclined planes.

EXAMPLES OF COAST EROSION

With a few exceptions, the effect of the action of the sea is to erode a coastline. That is to say, its capacity to break down and remove is greater than the capacity to deposit *at the water edge and above water level*. The exceptions to this rule are few, and are to be explained by such circumstances as an uplift of the land relative to the sea, to the rare cases of deposition, such as marshes or shingle banks, or to blown sands. The very nature of wave action must be on balance to erode.

Reference has been made already to erosion at the Covehithe and Dunwich cliffs in Suffolk. This is an extreme case, for all the factors favourable to erosion are present; soft cliffs, large surges, severe wave action and powerful coastwise currents. Erosion takes place elsewhere at a speed which depends upon the measure in which these factors are present.

Christchurch Bay

Among the interesting instances of erosion on our south coast (many of them seeming to the local habitants disastrous rather than interesting), perhaps the attack on the cliffs in Christchurch Bay is the most complex; certainly it appears to be very difficult to prevent. The bay, which lies between the entrance to Christchurch Harbour and Hurst Castle, is exposed to the full force of Atlantic gales, and there is a slight balance of current action to the eastward. The beach is backed by cliffs of gravel with Barton Clay beneath, but this clay bed dips from west to east, and disappears about half-way along the beach. Only during violent storms does wave action reach the cliffs, and then only at high spring tides; and here, as at Covehithe, the rate of erosion would be almost negligible but for the effect of storm surges. In the Channel the surges are smaller than in the North Sea, possibly not more than $2\frac{1}{2}$ feet. The comparatively small amplitude of the surges, combined with the sparse distribution of tide gauges, probably explains why they have not attracted so much attention as those in the North Sea. There is little doubt, however, that they are extremely important in the story of the erosion of our south coast.

If the surges are small they are just high enough to raise the level of wave action so that it reaches the cliffs at the back of the beach. At the western end, where there is clay at the foot of the cliffs, there is an unusual effect, for as the beach material is eroded, the cliff appears to slump in a way that forces the clay at the foot of the cliff outwards towards the sea. This clay is subsequently eroded, and more clay is then squeezed out towards the beach. The process is doubly unfortunate, for not only does the collapse of the cliffs push clay into the sea and thus hasten their erosion, but also this clay is on the move exactly where engineers might require foundations for coast defences, and this can be seen from some of the derelict groynes. The clay bed causes further embarrassment, being impervious; the sand resting on it is usually very wet so that during rainy seasons it slips and falls more readily than it would do if it were standing on a permeable formation.

Thus erosion is rapid; the currents and winds from the south-west transport the eroded material towards Hurst Point, and here it comes under the influence of the powerful ebb currents in the Solent which carry the shingle and sand so far to seaward that they are almost certainly irretrievably lost to the coastline.

These two instances of Christchurch and Benacre show how very rapid and serious erosion is brought about not by any one process, but by a combination of circumstances of widely differing kinds. But generally there are two distinct stages in the story; the first the breakdown of the coast by wave action, which can be hastened by the softness of the coast and by the occurrence of surges, and the second the lateral removal of the eroded material. Without the first there can clearly be no erosion; without the second the eroded material would lie offshore in such a position as to form protective banks which would resist further wave action and so prevent erosion.

There are, unfortunately, innumerable other places where erosion is taking place because of this same combination of wave and current action, possibly aggravated by the rising of sea level due to surges.

EXAMPLES OF DEPOSITION

So far we have considered a number of coastal changes, some of which involve removal of material from one place to another, such as a tombolo or a headland and others which are subtractions from the land by the sea. It has already been said that on balance the sea is a destructive force; but there are places where deposition is taking place, although they are relatively few. Apart from the emergence of large land masses due to earth movements, such features as deltas, spits and marshes are formed as additions to the land on whose shores they are formed. Deltas and spits have already been briefly discussed. The importance of marshes is their form, which is such that they can be reclaimed; their interest is in their speed and manner of growth.

The essence of marsh formation has been mentioned on p. 30. The original source of the material which helps to build them up is the fine material presented to the sea by rivers. The coarse material brought down by rivers may be quickly deposited on the sea bed or on the flanking beaches, but some material will be so fine that in the remote event of its ever subsiding on to a beach it will be stirred into suspension by the next onset of wave action. Thus, this very fine silt will settle very slowly. Some of it may find its way to the bed of a sea so deep that it will not be affected by wave action again and so will stay there; much of it will remain in suspension near the coastline until it can find somewhere where the wave action is so slight that it can at last settle.

This kind of shelter is to be found in our protected estuaries and in the water trapped in lagoons or behind bars. Such traps used to be made artificially with embankments and fascines during the reclamation of the fenlands of East Anglia, but there are many places where deposition is taking place unaided by man.

The rate of deposition depends of course upon the amount of silt in suspension; but if we assume that this is fairly constant over a period of years it is evident that the rate of growth is likely to decrease due to this cause as the marsh height increases because the tidal inundations will be smaller—that is, less deep—and in due course less frequent. The marsh will grow marsh plants appropriate to its level and these will hasten the rate of growth owing to the annual deposition of the dead foliage, and since the silt will settle more quickly among the marsh plants than in open water because of the extra shelter that they provide. Should there be any sand in the neighbourhood they will help to trap windblown sand. It is doubtful, however, whether this process can have much effect on the rate of growth of the marsh because blown sand must settle as readily on wet mud as on vegetation. The plants which grow in marshes naturally depend upon the climate. (In this country there is a considerable literature on the subject.)

As the marsh land approaches the level of high springs the rate of growth due to the accession of silt must decrease, and subsequent elevation must depend entirely upon the contributions made by wind and by the vegetation. By this time the marsh will begin to develop a drainage system, gullies having been cut by receding water during the fall of the tide. The rate of growth of marshes can be quite rapid; deposits of a centimetre per year are by no means uncommon.

The general process must always be the same; there may be differences in the kind of vegetation—particularly in tropical countries; on many coastlines the presence of mangroves is of paramount importance; equally the method of trapping may vary. The large marshes between Blakeney and Wells-next-the-Sea appear, at least at their western end near Bob Hall's sand, to owe their origin to a small ridge of coarse material, partly shingle, which was thrown up on this very flat beach. The gradient of Bob Hall's sand is about one in a thousand. How this narrow bank of shingle could have been formed along it will probably remain one of the mysteries of the Norfolk coastal movements; but once it was formed it became a new back of the beach, and silt was deposited on the landward side of it. The whole marsh promises to form one of the large natural gains from the sea round our coastline.

If the existence of this new back of beach is fundamental to the evolution of marshes at this particular point, it by no means provides a complete explanation of the process of reclamation; explanations of coastal phenomena can be simplified but they are rarely intrinsically simple. The small bank on Bob Hall's sand is important because the beach is so flat, and it is natural to ask why, at this place, west of the Blakeney Spit, there should be a gradient of one in a thousand when most sand beaches are about ten times as steep: the origin of the sand is obscure, it might be the final resting place of one of the many North Sea sandbanks which happened to be brought very close inshore at this point.

In conclusion, the formation of marshes requires an

existing protected shoal, calm water, and repeated coverings by silt-bearing water. In these conditions the sea bed can be raised to the level of high springs; at this stage the botanists are best qualified to complete the story.

CHAPTER VI

EVIDENCE OF CHANGES AND OBSERVATIONAL METHODS

IF we are to form sound judgments about coastal problems we must be cautious in our use of the evidence of changes, both past and present. We may well find that accounts of former changes are distorted by imagination or by the exaggeration which comes from frequent repetition, while present changes are not infrequently magnified because of the feelings of worried property owners. The fact that a church is now in the sea is clearly evidence of erosion, always provided that the identity of the church is beyond question; a house falling into the sea is also proof of erosion, while a sea wall or a sea cliff in an inland position is proof of deposition, or that the land is gaining from the sea.

But the evidence is not always so clear, especially when the coast is being eroded, for the simple reason that there is a high degree of probability that such marks as might have been of value have disappeared from sight beneath the sea.

Hearsay evidence is in any case notoriously unreliable, and should always be viewed with the greatest suspicion. Such sources are likely to mislead not only in respect of the amount of coastal change—the linear movement of a water line—which is difficult to assess; but the associated phenomena are to a large extent just as elusive, wave heights, wind and current velocities, and beach profiles

—all of these rapidly changing factors are often very wildly described.

Clearly, any evidence that we use must be provided by our own observation or someone else's. In the latter case we must do our best to assess its reliability; we must not discard it out of hand because some small defect is apparent, to do so might mean losing invaluable information; in the former case we must endeavour to make our observations as reliable as they can be in the particular circumstances of our enquiry.

An obvious source of information is maps. Not infrequently changes in a coastal feature can be plotted from maps of different dates, the differences in delineation representing the changes in the coastline. To argue in this way is justifiable if the maps are accurate, but whether the maps are to be relied upon depends upon several factors, the chief of which are the date of the map, its scale, and the purpose for which is was made. Most old maps were small in scale, and have a limited value for this reason alone; but, as is to be expected, they were also inaccurate because the techniques of map-making, and the instruments available, were very inferior to those of today. Many maps of three or four centuries ago were no more than intelligent compilations from a collection of information of a most sketchy kind.

And yet such maps are often of some use. For instance, Saxton's map of Suffolk shows a large headland immediately north of Southwold (see Fig. V.11). There can be little doubt that the configuration of this feature is wrong, and that its extent in an east to west direction is exaggerated; such exaggerations would be very natural to an observer who had seen it from the north or south, from which positions its perspective would enhance the prominence to seaward. But while we may suspect the shape and size of the headland, there is little reason to suspect its *position*, since it is shown to the south of Covehithe, which is plotted in the correct position. This fact of the *position* of the headland is of the greatest interest, since subsequent maps have shown it to be moving steadily northward, until now (1959) it is just south of Kessingland.

But on the whole, old maps yield little evidence of the finer details of coastlines; recent maps, which are plotted to a high degree of fidelity, are by contrast of the greatest value.

Large scale maps are much more useful than those of smaller scales; it should be remembered, however, that few countries are mapped in such detail as our own, and we are particularly fortunate to have such detailed and accurate maps as we have—a circumstance that those who complain of the slow rate of revision would do well to remember. It is possible to measure on a map 0·01 of an inch, and a good modern map would plot a well-defined line to this degree of accuracy. This means to say that the whereabouts of a point or line on a 1-inch map is plotted to an accuracy of about 50 feet, while a 1/2,500 map would yield a precision of about two feet. If, then, we consult the 1/2,500 maps of our coast at various dates we shall be able to gain a good idea of whether the coast is changing or not. In most parts of the country three surveys made within the last century will be available.

Some surveys are made, and some maps are drawn for reasons which are in no way connected with coastal problems. A road map or a town map may be so specialized that no effort has been made to portray coastal features with any degree of accuracy. Obviously such maps are of no use for our purposes.

It remains to consider what precise coastal details are surveyed; that is to say what lines of detail are plotted on the map. Usually there will be three lines, H.W.M.O.S.T., L.W.M.O.S.T. (High Water Mark and Low Water

Mark of Ordinary Spring Tides) and a third line at the back of the beach. H.W.M.O.S.T. is usually identified and surveyed with some care; the line of drift material for the appropriate tide is observed, and there is little difficulty in surveying it; the same can be said of the line at the back of the beach. The precise character of this line may vary widely, from the top of a cliff, to a sea wall or the boundary between sand and grass; but whatever it is, it is usually a clearly defined line, and the surveyor has no difficulty in fixing it. The same cannot be said of L.W.M.O.S.T. This line is more often than not covered by the sea; it is often removed from the rest of the survey by a wide expanse of sand which makes it a little more difficult to survey, and it is, moreover, a relatively unimportant feature for the ordinary user of Ordnance Survey Maps. Thus, while it would be reasonable to argue that a change in the mapped position of the line at the back of the beach, or of H.W.M.O.S.T. indicates a change in the coastline, the evidence of the line of L.W.M.O.S.T. should be used with some caution.

Another invaluable source of information is to be found in hydrographic charts, which, of course, are really maps of a special kind; but the fact that they are made for those who are primarily interested in the sea makes them of the greatest value to students of coastal phenomena.

There are a few points about marine charts which should be borne in mind, especially if they are being studied along with land maps of the same piece of coast. The first is that whereas it is the custom to produce a systematic series of maps of a country on the same scale, for instance our own 1-inch maps, no attempt is made to produce a series of charts of the same scale of the whole coastline of a country. To do so would be a waste of time. The coast will be surveyed on a scale appropriate to its importance for shipping; places like the Thames or the

Clyde, are mapped in great detail on large scales; charts on comparable scales will not be found for the West Coast of Ireland, where there are no great ports, and therefore no great amount of shipping. Yet it is surprising and indeed gratifying that our coastline has been surveyed in great detail by the Hydrographic Branch of the Admiralty, and the quality of the published charts is excellent.

Small scale charts, being as a rule on Mercator's projection, may have a variation in scale; but if the scale of degrees and minutes of latitude is used no problem arises.

It should be remembered too that whereas the datum level for land maps is usually means sea level, the datum plane for soundings is described as 'a plane so low that the tide will but seldom fall below it'.[1] This is variously interpreted by various countries; obviously there is some difficulty—but comparatively little importance—in a precise definition of it for small scale charts of large areas. For charts of small areas the datum plane is usually a little below the level of mean Low Water Springs. The relation between datum levels in this country and Ordnance Survey Datum levels is published in the *Admiralty Manual of Tides*. Heights on charts are given in feet above Mean High Water Springs.

The usefulness of Admiralty Charts for a study of coasts and coastal changes is limited only by their smallness of scale and the occasional lack of revision. The limitations of scale have already been dealt with, and it is apparent that there can be no evidence of change on a single chart; it is the differences between successive chartings that are significant. Hydrographic surveying—indeed any kind of surveying—is very expensive, and resurveys are undertaken only when they are necessary. On land, growing towns and other developments make map revision necessary. The reasons for revising nautical

[1] International Hydrographic Conference, 1926.

charts are of a different kind; here other changes are taking place. For instance, off Lowestoft, the narrow channels between large sandbanks move so quickly that the chart of those waters is revised nearly every year; for the same reason charts of the Thames Estuary are being constantly revised; these revisions do not often involve re-sounding the whole area of the chart, but are usually partial revisions of particular channels, often with the specific aim of deciding where navigational buoys should be moored.

Charts give full detail of the coastline, including the line of chart datum, the line of mean high water springs, the nature of the coast or beach, whether sand, shingle or rock; details of tidal streams, and, of course, soundings to the sea bed. Heights between high and low water are given as *drying heights* in feet above chart datum.

It cannot be strongly emphasized that charts are an invaluable source of information on coastal matters.

AIR PHOTOGRAPHS

Air photographs constitute a new and important source of information about beaches and coastlines. Unlike maps, these can be taken at short notice, subject to the weather and the availability of funds. After the floods of January–February 1953 the relevant parts of the east coast were photographed within a few days.

Air photographs can supply information which is both up to date and detailed. The scale of a vertical air photograph is f/H,

where f = the focal length of the camera used,

and H = the height of the plane above the ground.

Thus, in what may be called the normal conditions, using a camera with a 12-inch lens ($f = 1$ foot), and flying at a height of 10,000 feet, the scale would be 1/10,000. If the photographs were 9×9 inches in size, the area covered would be $1 \cdot 2 \times 1 \cdot 2$ miles. The scale, and the area to be covered, can be varied by the choice of camera and flying height.

Few students of coastlines could incur the expense of chartering a plane to take photographs; the cost is considerable; but many local authorities and public bodies have libraries of photographs, and investigators should consult them whenever it is desirable to do so. The information which may be gained from them depends so much upon the photographs and the conditions in which they are taken that only the most general observations can be made upon what is clearly a very wide subject.

It is highly probable that the air photographs will be on a larger scale than the existing charts. This is in itself a great advantage, especially as the camera records *everything* which comes into view. Thus features which have come into existence since the chart was made, or minor features, such as runnels and bars, under-water bars, mud patches, and seaweed, may be revealed which, for quite obvious reasons, were not plotted on the charts. It is interesting that not infrequently the runnel and bar formation,[1] when the amplitude of the runnels is small, have been observed on air photographs for the first time; and what has not come to the notice of an observer on the beach has been very clear on air photographs. Air photographs provide unique evidence of other factors which may be of great importance; of wave patterns and breaker lines; of underwater rocks and bars, or of rip currents.

If there are advantages in using air photographs because their scales are large, a problem may well arise because it is often difficult to evaluate the scale. The value, scale $= f/H$ cannot often give a precise result,[2]

[1] See p. 116.
[2] If photographs are taken with survey cameras which have been calibrated a reliable figure for f is usually available; if not this may be suspect, especially if f is large, say 20 or 36 inches.

since the flying height H is rarely known to any degree of reliability. Moreover, the photographs, not being truly vertical, may suffer from tilt distortion. The usual method of assessing the scale of the photographs is to compare measurements taken on them with measurements between the same features on the best map or chart available. Such measurements should be taken along both axes of the photographs (possibly yielding two different scales because of tilt) and clearly the precision of the result will depend upon the scale and quality of the maps, and of the proportion of land to water on the photographs. If the picture covers a large amount of water it may be almost impossible to determine its scale.

Usually one is fortunate to have any photographs at all; but if one should ever be in the happy position of being able to commission photographs to be taken the most careful thought should be given to deciding the scale. The scale selected will be a compromise between the advantages of the detail of a large scale, and the wide cover of a small one. Then there are different kinds of film; the usual panchromatic film gives very good tone rendering; infra-red by itself is not so useful as panchromatic film, though it can sometimes produce additional information, while the advantages of colour film are tremendous. Such film was used during the war of 1939–45, and interpretation problems were vastly simplified by it.

When the interpretational and geometrical aspects of air photographs are understood, much can be achieved by the judicious taking of photographs at particular times or in special circumstances. If information is required about the nature of the whole beach, photographs should be taken at low tide, and preferably at low spring tides, so as to get the maximum possible exposure of the beach. The times and dates of these low tides can be worked out from the Admiralty Tide Tables; the reader must not be surprised if in winter the lowest spring tides always occur during hours of darkness or thereabouts! A very simple method of contouring a beach was first used during the war, and has been used since on beaches where the surf makes small boat work difficult. The beach was photographed at prearranged times, at high and low springs, and at as many intermediate stages (usually four) as were required. The times were carefully

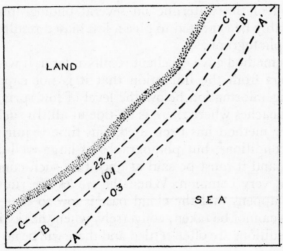

FIG. VI.1.—Contours of a beach, transferred from air photographs.

recorded, and the heights of the water level at these times were computed from the tide tables. In Fig. VI.1 these are represented by 0·3, 10·1 and 22·4 feet. Then the corresponding water lines, AA′, BB′, CC′, etc., were transferred to a master drawing from the photograph. Any number of contours can of course be drawn in this way, always provided that the necessary photographs have been taken.

With care results of surprising accuracy are attainable; obviously the water levels must be computed with care, but there seems at first sight to be an even more alarming source of error; that is to ascertain the precise position of the waterline. This moves appreciably in a horizontal sense with the incoming and outgoing of the waves so that there may be an ambiguity of position proportional to the height of the waves. For this reason photographs should be taken if possible when the sea is calm. Errors due to this cause may be further reduced by taking photographs with a large overlap so that any point on the beach is photographed four or five times. The mean position of the waterline on several photographs may reasonably be expected to give a less biased result than a single photograph.

This method gave excellent results as far as it went, but it suffers from the limitation that it is not capable of yielding information below the level of low spring tides or on beaches where there is no tide at all. In such cases another method has been used, this time requiring not calm conditions, but photographs of large well-defined waves, and it must be said at once that such conditions are not very common. When the waves are running it often happens that the cloud base is low so that photographs cannot be taken; conversely, when the sky is clear the conditions are often settled and there will be no waves.

The expression $C^2 = \dfrac{g\lambda}{2\pi} \tanh \dfrac{2\pi d}{\lambda}$ . . . (4)

shows that the depth of the sea can be deduced if we know the wave length and the wave velocity at a given point, always assuming that only one wave system is in existence. Plate V would be an excellent photograph for the purpose. If we can give a scale to our photographs we can measure wave lengths, and if we know the camera interval, that is, the lapse of time between exposures, we can compute the velocities of the wave crests. For instance, if at a given point the wave length is 100 feet and the wave velocity 15 feet per second it can be seen from Appendix A that the depth is 7 feet. The method admits of a solution if (as unfortunately is often the case) the camera interval is not known by working in terms of wave lengths and wave periods. An example is given in Appendix B.

The method, which was used extensively during the war, and has been used since then on French Moroccan beaches, where surf conditions are severe, has obvious limitations. The first is that wave crests are often indistinct and vague, so that measurements, especially in deep water, lack precision. Moreover, a glance at the curves in Appendix A shows that for short waves the expression becomes insensitive for depths greater than ten feet.

It is now a commonplace that air photographs should be examined as stereoscopic pairs rather than singly. Stereoscopic viewing of pairs of photographs gives a picture in relief which conveys much more than the two-dimensional information provided by a single photograph. There is no space here to explain that it is possible to obtain three-dimensional quantities by stereoscopic examination of air photographs; many maps based on air photographs have reliable contours as well as the usual detail in plan. The methods used for contouring land have been applied to the surface of the sea, notably by Schumacher and Hidaka, who have produced contoured maps of sea waves. The results are interesting, and useful information may be forthcoming from such methods when the obvious difficulties of scale, tilt effects and interpretation are overcome.

For highly organized researches, where finance is no problem, an intelligent use of air photographs can be of the greatest use; those who are working at more modest levels should endeavour to obtain access to any photographs which may have been taken.

So far in this chapter we have considered the value of information that may be available from existing sources or which might be collected from other agencies. Valuable though this information may be, there will inevitably be in any problem much that the research worker can do for himself. The exact observations that he can make will inevitably depend upon his resources in time, instruments, and skill. The more detailed, the more frequent, and the more comprehensive his observations the better.

Surveys

These may be either land surveys or marine surveys, the former being of the kind usually made by the ordinary land surveyor, and the latter by the hydrographic surveyor. The very fact that we are surveying the coastline inevitably means that both must to some extent be modified to suit the special circumstances, and there will be occasions when the two of them overlap.

If a coastline is changing, especially if it includes such features as cliff tops, cliff bottoms, and well-defined high-water marks, periodic surveys on suitable scales will provide excellent evidence of the changes. The surveys can be made, according to the special circumstances of the terrain, by the conventional methods of triangulation, traversing, plane tabling or chain surveys. Whatever method is used it is of paramount importance that the work be based on permanent and unmistakable ground marks so that the continued co-ordination and control of the work is assured. This simple but important point needs emphasis. It would be folly to base the survey of a piece of coastline on marker pegs which could be removed by a single storm; to do so would be to waste all the effort that had been put into the work before the storm.

The evidence of plans alone is, however, limited by the very fact that a third dimension is not included. Heights and depths can be ascertained by levelling or by soundings. When their positions are known, contours can be drawn. Often there are reasons for not contouring such plans, and it is usually found convenient for the study of beach changes to draw profiles or sections at selected points. Fig. V.5 shows profiles which have been surveyed at intervals at a point near Blackpool. It is one of a number of such sections which have been surveyed at points carefully plotted on large-scale plans. If sufficient sections have been surveyed the rate of accretion or erosion can be computed and such a series of sections is excellent evidence of the nature of the changes taking place. It should be noted, however, that although this kind of evidence is of great value, it is all too often limited because the time intervals between surveys are too long. One would like to know exactly when and in what circumstances the changes which have occurred actually took place.

Profiles of the kind shown in Fig. V.5 are best surveyed by simple levelling. As has been mentioned before, it is imperative that terminal marks be permanent, and if possible concealed from the attention of visitors to the coast whose curiosity or irresponsibility seems to urge them to uproot any stake or mark that may be found near the beach. It will usually be found convenient to plot sections with reference to Ordnance Survey height datum by levelling from the nearest benchmark; subsequent reference to chart datum may be made, if necessary, by referring to the correlation given in the Tide Tables. Sections should be taken as far to seaward as possible. The best time to survey therefore is at low springs; and very useful sections can be drawn if the staff holder can get out to a depth of five or six feet. Beyond this depth a boat and other methods become necessary.

Experience has shown that sections taken to a depth of 5 or 6 feet below low springs are usually inadequate for a proper understanding of coastal changes. Much may be learned from them, but the zone of wave action, particularly during storms, goes much further to seaward than this, and the writer has formed the opinion that in the North Sea the observations should be taken to a depth of three fathoms. Where larger waves are encountered changes will take place at proportionally greater depths.

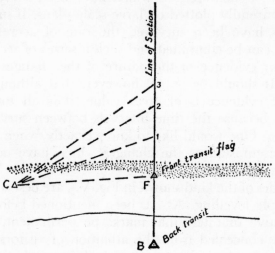

FIG. VI.2.—Method of fixing soundings by plane table.

Observations to such depths can be made by extending the profile sections already described by soundings. A simple and convenient method of doing this is shown in Fig. VI.2. Poles or flags are put up as back and fore 'transits', and the boat is kept on this line. From a previously fixed side point C cross-bearings are taken; this can be done very conveniently with the help of a plane table oriented on CF, to the points 1, 2, 3, etc., at which soundings are taken. The only difficulty or rather risk in doing this is a possible misunderstanding between the observer at C and the boat party as to when soundings are taken, but this is a matter calling for a sensible system of signals. The important point is that a ray C3 should be drawn exactly when the sounding is taken. It then remains to determine the correction to be applied to the soundings in order to reduce them to M.S.L. or to any other datum plane. But whatever plane is chosen the process will be the same; it will be necessary to apply a correction whose magnitude will be the difference between M.S.L. and the selected datum plane. This can be done by levelling from a point whose height is known, to the mean sea surface. This will give the height of the

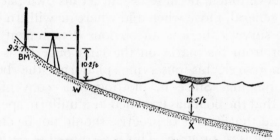

Fig. VI.3.—Reducing soundings to datum.

sea at any given time with reference to M.S.L.; the correction is then made quite simply. For instance, let us suppose that all heights are to be referred to Ordnance Datum, or M.S.L. At a given time a sounding of 12·5 is taken. See Fig. VI.3. At the same time—within proper limits—it is ascertained by levelling that the sea level at W is 10·2 feet below the level of a temporary bench mark BM, whose height is 9·2 feet. The level of the sea therefore is $(9·2 - 10·2) = - 1·0$ feet O.D. and the depth of the sounding at $X - 1·0 - 12·5 = - 13·5$ feet.

HYDROGRAPHIC SURVEYS

There may well be circumstances in which a chart of the whole sea bed is a much more useful document than a series of sections. This would be the case if a large area were under investigation. Charts surveyed at intervals, especially if plotted on a transparent medium such as Kodatrace, provide an excellent means for ascertaining what changes have take place on the sea bed. The usefulness of the charts will be enhanced if their scales are large, and if the soundings are closely spaced. The organization and execution of a hydrographic survey must, from the very nature of things, be more complex than a survey of a comparable area of land, especially as the time factor is involved. On land a single surveyor can achieve much, because he can set his own pace, and can, in general, move when and where he will. In hydrographic surveys there is an obvious detachment of the surveyor from his marks on the land once he is in his boat; moreover, his observing platform, the boat, is always moving. Since in plotting it is convenient to assume that the boat has travelled at a uniform speed it is important that its rate of progress should not be changed while work is in progress. This is a counsel of perfection, and conditions of wind and tide create real difficulties. The whole programme of work will be much slower and much more complicated if it cannot be assumed that the speed of the boat has been constant. The following brief account of a method of survey which has been used with success is given for those who may be daunted at the thought of attempting hydrographic surveys.

In Fig. VI.4 A, B, C and D represent shore stations whose positions have been fixed as near to the back of the beach as possible, by any conventional survey methods. They are flagged, and back transits, on the lines of soundings, are put up at A′, B′ C′ and D′, and the bearings of AA′, BB′, etc., must be determined. It will be found convenient to level the heights of A, B, C and D, since it will be necessary to find the water level as has been explained on p. 167. At each station subtense marks are put up at S_1 and S_2, as shown on the line BB, in

Fig. VI.4. The length of these subtense bases will depend upon the length of the lines to be sounded; for lines half a mile long a base of 200 feet is convenient; that is 100 feet on each side of the line. The soundings can now commence. The surveyor with his sextant measures the angle included by S_1S_2 as the boat proceeds shorewards from

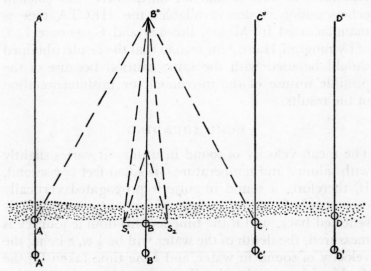

FIG. VI.4.—Fixing soundings by angles taken by one observer.

the end of the line B″; note that only *one* sextant angle is necessary as long as the helmsman keeps the boat on line. In this way the distances of the soundings from B, etc., can be determined; the depths can be reduced to datum by the method already described. If the boat is stopped at the seaward end of the line angles AB″B and BB″C can be observed, giving fixes of B″, C″, etc.; this will be a useful check on the work and especially on the bearings of the lines.

The amateur would usually take his soundings with a hand lead line; a lead about ten pounds in weight will be found convenient, and it is important that when reading the line it should be vertical, or 'up and down', a condition not always easy to achieve, especially if there should be a cross current.

If it is possible to procure an echo-sounder, much time and labour can be saved. A brief account of the underlying principles of the echo-sounder is given for two reasons. The first is that an inexpensive and efficient echo-sounder is now available; the HECTA type is manufactured by Messrs. Brookes and Gatehouse Ltd. of Lymington, Hants,[1] the second that the results obtained should be used with the same caution because of the possible misuse of the instrument or misinterpretation of the results.

ECHO SOUNDING

The mean velocity of sound in water—it varies slightly with salinity and temperature—is 4,800 feet per second. If, therefore, a sound impulse is propagated vertically downwards from the surface of the water so that it is reflected back, and if the time for this double journey is measured, the depth of the water will be $\frac{1}{2} vt$, v being the velocity of sound in water, and t the time taken for the double journey. In detail the apparatus is complex because of the necessity for carefully controlling the instant of emission of the signal, and also because the return signal is so weak that it needs amplification in just the same way as a radio signal is amplified; there are other minor complications, too; for instance, the signal cannot be emitted from the surface of the sea, but the transmitter must be submerged to some extent.

If we neglect these complications and refinements the instrument can be simply explained; in Fig. VI.5 the signal is sent out from the transmitter T in the hull of

[1] The inexpensive instrument is not self-recording, soundings are indicated on a dial. The description given here is for the more elaborate instrument; the underlying principles are of course the same for both instruments.

the boat; at the instant of transmission an impulse is given to the stylus of the recording device. This consists of a roll of suitably sensitized paper the end of which, PP′ is pulled downwards by rollers at a uniform speed. The stylus T′ is at the end of a revolving arm OT′; and revolves at about 500 revolutions per minute.

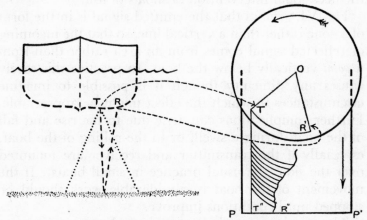

FIG. VI.5.—Principles of echo-sounder.

When the arm is in the position OT′ the impulse which was given at the instant of transmission of the signal causes the stylus to make a mark, and this mark continues until the signal is returned from the bottom to the receiver R in the hull of the boat. At this instant the stylus, which has rotated to R′, ceases to record, so that T′R′ on the recording paper is a function of the depth of the water. By the time the arm completes the revolution the paper has moved on slightly—so has the boat—and another mark is made. Thus, the trace T′T″ represents the surface of the water and R′R″ a profile of the sea bed. The instrument should be calibrated every day against soundings made with a lead line; it will be seen that the interval T′R′ can be measured on a scale of feet, fathoms or metres, and that calibration of the instrument can be simply effected by adjusting the length T'R' to the lead line depth; this requires only a slight turn of the governor control which varies the speed of rotation of the stylus arm.

The records are usually very easy to interpret in spite of double and sometimes treble echoes, and in spite of the occasional intervention of shoals of fish.

Fig. VI.5 shows that the emitted signal is in the form of a cone rather than a vertical line, so that the incoming or reflected signal comes from an area rather than from a *point* vertically below the boat. In practice this rarely causes any difficulty though it is possible to imagine circumstances in which the effect might be appreciable. Further complications can arise due to the rise and fall of the boat during a swell, or to the rolling of the boat, especially if the transmitter and receiver are mounted over the side (the usual practice in small boats). If the movement of the boat is considerable work should be stopped until conditions improve.

The number of periodic or repeated surveys made by the Hydrographic Department of the Admiralty on our coastline is comparatively small; few surveys have been made by other agencies. The reason is clear; they cannot be made without skill, nor without determination and enthusiasm. Until recently there was no national organization which attempted to make such surveys: even now the total resources for making them are so small that there seems little hope that the evidence which is so vital for a proper understanding of the coastal problems can be forthcoming in sufficient quantities. Accurate surveys are the very essence of the evidence needed.

WAVE MEASUREMENTS

If a single well-defined wave train is running the period can be measured quite simply with a watch, and the length at any depth can be determined by means of Appendix B. But heights are much more difficult to measure. Reference has already been made to an ingenious wave recorder devised by Dr. Deacon, which is a kind of inverted echo-sounder. That is to say, the transmitter and receiver are on the sea bed and the echo is received from the water/air surface. The resultant record of wave height and lengths is such that an analysis can be made which reveals the various constituent wave systems. The results of this method of recording and analysis are important, and have been used in order to locate storm centres and to predict the times of arrival of large waves.

Simpler methods of measuring wave heights will doubtless occur to the reader. For instance, encouraging results have been obtained by observing the angular rise and fall of a buoy moored at a known distance from the point of observation; the results of this method may of course be affected by the horizontal movement of the buoy. In any measurement of wave height it should be remembered that the amplitude of waves increases appreciably as they approach the plunge point; it has been observed that just before breaking the amplitude may be 30 per cent greater than in deep water. If, therefore, wave heights are measured inshore, the measurement will be of little significance if the steepening effect is not taken into account. Wave heights measured near a sea wall where reflections cause a clapotis effect, may be very misleading.

MEASUREMENT OF CURRENT VELOCITIES AND DIRECTIONS

Our knowledge of the water flow on our coasts, whether due to tidal streams or currents due to other causes, is very meagre. The information given on charts, valuable though it is, is usually widely spaced; the stations at which observations have been made are usually in deep water, and the velocities given are in all probability for the top 30 feet of the water, this being the water layer in which ships move.

The most rapid changes take place in the lesser depths inshore; here the current velocities are almost certainly reduced because of the shoaling of the water; the movement at the surface is not necessarily of the same magnitude or in the same direction as that on the bottom (indeed it may well be in the opposite direction as has been explained elsewhere), and the behaviour may well vary rapidly from place to place as well as from time to time. No factor in coastal problems varies more rapidly in time, more widely in amount, or is so difficult to measure on some occasions as water movement.

Bearing in mind that we need to measure the water movement because it is the transporting agent of sand and shingle which it holds in suspension, it is highly desirable that the measurements be made if possible when the greatest amount of material is in suspension, that is, during storms. At such times it is not possible to make observations from a boat; a small boat would not survive, and the depths are too small for a large vessel; in any case the vital area for observations is probably in surf. Self recording instruments, some of which will be described briefly, are unlikely to produce accurate results. There are difficulties in mooring them, and in spite of the claims of the makers and inventors they are not likely to produce results in the worst, and therefore most important conditions. There is another difficulty; electronic and radio devices must for obvious reasons be very expensive; the consequences of this are twofold; first, if the apparatus can be bought at all, only one or two instruments are likely to be available, so that *simultaneous* observations at several places are not likely to be forthcoming. The second difficulty is the real anxiety of using valuable, but inconspicuous apparatus in the sea where it may be roughly handled by fishermen who, with their minds on their nets and their fishing in general, may inadvertently sweep it up in a trawl. There is a real risk in leaving any kind of apparatus unattended, even if it is marked by a buoy.

What is needed is a simple, cheap device which will measure the depth on or near the bottom, as well as at lesser depths, which will give results in any condition of wind and sea. As far as is known, no such device exists. In the following pages a variety of current measuring devices are described, and their relative merits are assessed. The reader may be able to employ some of them, possibly modified, in the particular circumstances of his investigation.

FLOAT OBSERVATIONS, DESCRIBED BY HYDRO-GRAPHIC SURVEYORS AS DRIFTING LOGSHIPS

If we measured the distance travelled by a floating object and recorded the time taken to travel that distance, it would be possible to compute the rate of travel of the object, and this would indicate the water velocity *on the surface*, assuming that the float were not affected by the wind.

A suitably designed logship will give a fair indication of velocities at depth. Fig. VI.6 shows the pattern which is often used. A is a float, with flag, to which observations are made, and the float is made as small as possible. Its function is to support the canvas vane B, but its resistance to the water should be negligible in comparison with that of the vane so that the movement indicated by the flag represents the movement at the predetermined depth, and not that at the surface. The flag must be small so that the whole ship is not affected by wind. A light for night work could be attached. Such a device has the

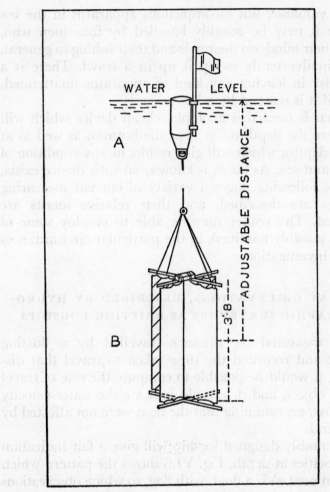

WATER LEVEL

A

ADJUSTABLE DISTANCE

3'8

B

Fig. VI.6.—Admiralty type logships.

advantage over a vertical pole that whereas the pole will indicate the mean velocity of the water over the whole of its length, the logship will give results over a narrower range of depth if a suitable size and depth setting of the vane is made.

In suitable conditions the logship could be 'streamed'

from a boat: that is to say, it could be paid out on a line, and the length of line so paid out during a given time, measured on a stop-watch, would give the velocity. It is customary to mark the line at 10-foot intervals, since 10 feet per minute = 0·1 knot.

Should the sea be too rough for boat work the logship may be allowed to drift free, and simultaneous bearings can be taken to it, at pre-arranged times from two shore stations. The positions at the known times being plotted, the rate of travel can be computed. It will doubtless occur to the reader that there may be some difficulty in launching the logship in rough weather. This is a very real problem, and is a clear limitation to the usefulness of the method.

Mechanical Current Meters

There are a number of current meters designed primarily for measuring velocities in rivers or channels where the direction of flow is known, being determined by the configuration of the channel, and where it is to be assumed that rough water will not hamper operations. Although at first sight they may present differing appearances, the principle involved is the same. The meter is fixed; a vane or rudder causes it to lie head-on to the current, and as the current streams past it, a propeller, or wheel with cups, rather like an anemometer, is caused to rotate. This rotating unit is calibrated in order to ascertain the amount of horizontal water movement per revolution. The Ekman meter has propeller blades; the Watt, an arrangement of cups, while the Ott instrument has a helical screw. The revolutions are counted either by a recording device on the instrument itself or by impulses, usually at each tenth revolution, which are carried to earphones worn by the observer.

Such instruments, which can be set to any depth, can yield excellent results when sea conditions are favourable, but it is quite impossible to use them when boat work is difficult.

Naval hydrographers use a larger and more robust instrument which gives readings up to six knots. The instrument is self recording; one pen records the speed in knots on a paper chart mounted on a drum, while a series of dots indicate the magnetic bearings at suitable intervals. As the water passes the instrument it tilts a heavy plate by an amount which depends upon its velocity, and this tilt is recorded by the pen. The instrument is calibrated in a tank before use, the angle of tilt of the plate obviously increasing with the increase in velocity. This instrument has the advantage of being robust, simple and entirely self contained; moreover the clock drive will run for eight days. Its size and weight make it unsuitable for inshore work, and there are the usual difficulties of mooring it or fixing it in surf conditions.

The Roberts Radio Current Meter, which has been developed by the United States Coast and Geodetic Survey, has as its essential current measuring unit a mechanical current meter with a four bladed propeller. It also embodies a magnetic compass. These are suspended from a floating raft with a radio transmitter which sends signals indicating the velocity and direction of the stream to a shore station at frequent intervals.

It is claimed that the instrument will work in rough seas; but its cost, measured in thousands of pounds, is such that few organizations could afford one, let alone risk such a valuable instrument in surf.

Of the instruments and devices so far described, only one, the logship, seems to offer any practical solution of the problem; the others eliminate themselves because of their cost, and because of the difficult and hazardous conditions in which the observations must be made. If suitable logships could be fired by a catapult, rocket, or small mortar into the roughest seas their positions could be fixed by bearings from shore stations. There would be difficulties in detail in such operations, but there seems to be no satisfactory alternative to some such procedure.

OTHER SIMPLE OBSERVATIONAL METHODS

Dr. Carruthers has used an ingenious method of current measurement with success. The principle is simple. A bottle is partly filled with a liquid jelly—an ordinary fruit jelly will do. The jelly must be hot and liquid. He also puts into the bottle a small floating magnetic compass. When this bottle is moored by one end to a sinker on the sea bed the jelly sets; the angle of the surface of the jelly, being a function of the inclination of the bottle, is a good indicator of the velocity of the stream. For instance, in still water, the bottle will float vertically, in very rapid currents it will assume an almost horizontal position. The compass, set in the jelly, gives the direction of flow. Calibration can be done very simply by putting the bottles in a channel in a laboratory where the water velocities can be controlled and measured.

This method has produced very satisfactory results, and Dr. Carruthers is of the opinion that the jelly would set in a manner so as to yield satisfactory results even in surf. If this is so, its scope is considerable, for it has the advantages of economy and simplicity. There remain, however, the problems of heating the jelly, projecting the bottles into the sea and subsequently recovering them.

I am indebted to Mr. N. Alexander for another method which has the advantages of simplicity and robustness, and which if planted in the sea before a storm might yield valuable results while it was raging. The method has been found satisfactory in model tanks, but has not, as far as I am aware, been used in the sea.

The apparatus consists of a heavy sinker to which is moored a buoy. This buoy is connected to a second buoy by a chain whose length and weight are predetermined by the water depth and the velocities likely to be encountered. During slack water the weight of the chain will draw the buoys together; but as the current increases, so the distance between them will increase. This distance is therefore a function of the water velocity, it can be measured by simple survey methods, and the apparatus could be calibrated quite simply.

The method has the disadvantage that only *surface* velocities are measured, and there would appear to be a risk that the chains might foul on the turn of the tide. The method is not suitable for measurements in very shallow water.

The reader may regard these last two methods as being far-fetched; but they are at least inexpensive and are capable of producing results. Adequate records of water movement are extremely difficult to obtain, and it is probably no exaggeration to say that no single coastal investigation has been furnished with the barest minimum of reliable current observations. The writer has not infrequently heard supposed authorities arguing with heat on important coastal problems when it was all too obvious that they were in complete ignorance of the essential factor of water movement—and in consequence of the movement of material. This is a great and alarming gap in our competence to deal with coastal problems.

RADIO-ACTIVE METHODS

The importance of current observations, which have been discussed at some length, is that they indicate the direction in which the bed-material is likely to be carried. In the past attempts have been made to observe the movement of the material itself; sand traps have been made for measuring sand movement, but with little success, and marked shingle has been used in order to study shingle movement, with limited success.

Following a successful experiment with radio-active sand in the Thames, Steers and Smith made experiments in the sea at Scolt with radio-active pebbles. Davidson has done similar work on a curved spit of sand in Denmark, and Kidson near Orfordness. In each case it has been possible to trace the movement *of the material itself*, which is, of course, a conclusive observation, and goes one stage further than the current observations which must always leave some doubt as to whether material of a given size is in fact being moved by the current or not.

The general method of using radio-active methods is simply described. When the sand or shingle has been rendered radio-active—which calls for highly specialized assistance—it is planted in the required position, and this position is fixed by the usual means, either by re-section or by intersection from shore stations. Its subsequent movement is followed by sweeping with a specially adapted Geiger counter; this requires some skill and experience in interpreting signals; when the signal is received the position is fixed in the usual way.

It is probably too early to assess the value of the method, but the evidence is that it has a limited usefulness; the important factors appear to be:

(1) Its cost. So far the preparation of the radio-active sand and shingle has been very expensive.

(2) Risks. The authorities concerned impose restrictions on the places where the material may be planted and on the kind of isotypes used because of the possible danger to the public by radiation. Only isotopes with a very short half-life may be employed for obvious reasons.

(3) Scale. The very fact of cost at present limits the scale on which the observations can be made.

(4) *Range of detection.* At present no signal is reached unless the detector sweep is within $1\frac{1}{2}$ feet of the planted shingle or sand. Even assuming that sweeps are made six feet wide, a limit of distance of detection of nine feet is very small for boat work. With a wide dispersion of material after a storm, and assuming some difficulty in interpreting signals, it might be very difficult to pick up the material.

It may be that in time improvements in the method may render it cheaper and more practicable. Inman and Chamberlain have conducted an experiment with sand. Quartz sand was subjected to slow neutron irradiation, and then placed in the area. The movement of the quartz was traced by collecting samples of the bottom sediments after pre-arranged times and assaying for phosphorus -32, this being the principal radioisotope formed from the slow neutron irradiation of natural quartz sands.

The advantages claimed are that quartz sands of density and grain comparable with the natural sands can be used, and that there is no health hazard. It is said that the sensitivity of detection was about 1 grain in 100,000. The disadvantages are that even such a sensitivity would be insufficient to trace sand movement during large storms; it is well known that the rate of travel would cause much too rapid a dispersal. Further, highly specialized laboratory facilities are required.

As far as is known magnetic methods have not been seriously tried, but they would seem to offer distinct possibilities. Magnetic 'pebbles' could be made by inserting iron fragments into some lighter medium, such as wood or a resin glue, to make the particle density equal to that of flint which is 2·6. These pebbles could then be traced by means of a mine detector suitably modified. The method would be inexpensive and simple, but the range of detection might not be very high.

WIND OBSERVATIONS

Wind, either directly or indirectly, is responsible for moving most of the materials when coastal changes occur. The direct action of blowing sand on beaches or on dunes—or away from them—is small compared with the indirect effect wrought by waves and currents which, in turn, have been generated by the action of the winds on the sea. The results are dealt with in Chapter IV, but it is necessary at this stage to say something about the measurements of wind behaviour.

The information required is of two kinds; first the *historical* or long term statement of prevailing winds; their directions, mean velocities and frequencies of velocities. This kind of information which in this country is given in the publications of the Meteorological Office and the Air Ministry is of the utmost importance in any attempt to assess the importance of the exposure, or the aspect of a beach. Thanks to the official publications which are available in all civilized countries this kind of information is usually available.

There are times, however, when it is important to know the strength and direction of the wind at a specified hour. The direction of the coastal drift at a given time may be dominated by the wind; in the absence of other information wave sizes can be computed by means of Appendix C from wind strength and fetch, if both are ascertainable. Official publications, and indeed official observations, are of little help in such circumstances. The stations are often too far apart to permit of reliable interpolation of quantities which vary as rapidly in time and place as wind velocities. The author has not infrequently found that his own observations, taken on a beach, have shown little agreement with those recorded at meteorological stations 20 or 30 miles away.

Unfortunately the matter is not in our hands entirely; that is to say the problem cannot be solved by the observer on the beach because the waves and currents are not generated by the winds at the observer's position but by those to windward of him—and possibly by those a long way to windward.[1]

There will however be occasions on which the observer will wish to make his own wind observations. These can be made with the help of an anemometer. Portable instruments are made which yield quite good results. The anemometer is more important than the gust recorder; the maximum velocities in gusts are of interest, but they are of less significance than the mean wind movement.

It is possible to purchase these instruments from reputable manufacturers, and the instructions given with them are quite clear.

[1] It will of course be realized that very often the operative waves and currents are entirely unconnected with local winds.

CHAPTER VII

SEA DEFENCES

IF a piece of coastline is soft, and is attacked by destructive waves in circumstances which combine to remove the eroded material—such as surges or considerable longshore drifting—the coastline will retreat. It is almost certain that what is happening is a shoreward advance of the whole coastal profile (see Fig. VII.1). It

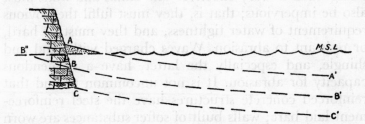

Fig. VII.1.—The process of erosion, showing that the whole sea bed is lowered from AA' to BB' and then to CC' etc.

is often not realized that this is so; too often the erosion is assumed to be an advance of the water edge, unrelated to the sea bed behind it. The evidence is probably falling cliffs, diminishing dunes, or the exposure of substrata not hitherto seen; but whatever the evidence may be, the fact is quite simply that the sea is beginning to advance upon the land; and any defences, if they are to be effective, must halt this process over the whole field of its activity.

The remedies most frequently applied are walls, banks,

and groynes. Walls and banks are erected as barriers to the sea; structures which are designed (supposedly) to deny it any further advance. The function of groynes is different; they are so constructed that they trap and hold the loose beach material and prevent its removal, and at the same time trap material which is brought to the area —laterally—from outside. Thus the effect of groynes is to retain on the beach material which would otherwise have left it, and to prevent the passage of what would otherwise have travelled across it. Groynes are often used in conjunction with walls and banks.

If banks and walls are to serve their purpose they must have stability, so that they cannot be moved, and this is almost synonymous with weight, but not quite; relatively slight structures, if well anchored—such as metal sheet piling—can be very effective. The banks and walls must also be impervious; that is, they must fulfil the obvious requirement of water tightness, and they must be hard, or resistant to abrasion. Waves charged with sand and shingle, and especially the latter, have a tremendous capacity for abrasion. It is not uncommon to find that reinforced concrete structures have the steel reinforcement laid bare; walls built of softer substances are worn away even more rapidly. We shall see later that designers of sea walls sometimes go further than these considerations of permanence and try to construct them in such a way that they reduce the energy of the waves.

Coast protection works of whatever kind can confer only local benefits, and it is almost true to say that they are likely to be harmful to the neighbouring coastline, especially to leeward. This is at once apparent if we consider the effect of groyning. If the groynes on a given length of coast have the effect of retaining sand and shingle which would otherwise have passed to a place to leeward, that place has been deprived of some of its material, and it follows that the rate of erosion there must be accelerated. It can often be seen that there is acute erosion at the end of sea walls because the unprotected part of the coast retreats relative to the wall and this causes local scouring which may proceed at a very rapid rate. It is therefore extremely important in designing coast protection schemes to give careful thought to the 'end effect'; that is to say, the scouring or denudation which can take place where a solid structure ends, giving place to a relatively soft beach.

There is another reason for giving careful attention to the limits of coast protection schemes, and this was demonstrated very clearly on the Norfolk coast during the floods of 1953. The sea defences were designed to resist wave action from the sea. But when the surge occurred the protecting banks were enfiladed; there were considerable floods on the landward side, and the water was so deep that, in the high winds prevailing, waves were generated which destroyed the banks from behind.

Banks

Banks have been used for some centuries as a means of coast protection; they are a feature of the reclamation schemes in Holland, and provide a natural means of defence. Surely the first instinct of man would be to use the materials at hand to build a barrier to hold back the invading water. The modern technique of sand-bagging is an obvious development from the earlier idea of earth banks. It is the method used by the Romans in the Fens and on Romney Marsh, and has been practised the world over since then.

Often it is associated with, if not preceded by, the process of 'warping'. This consists of putting down anything which tends to reduce the flow of the water and its consequent scour. Sods are used and faggots or fascines. Where they can be found locally faggots are still used by engineers in the early stages of reclamation schemes;

they are frequently used by French engineers on the coast of Brittany.

Andries Vierlingh, the Dutch engineer, writing in about 1575, constantly advocates a steady, almost cunning use of local materials in small barriers against the invading sea. He writes:

'Your foe Oceanus does not sleep by day or night, but comes suddenly like a roaring lion, seeking to devour the whole land. To have kept your country is a great victory won. God has given us by His Grace the materials to fight the sea. They are willow-twigs, grass-turfs, clay and straw, and we must use them intelligently and subtly.'

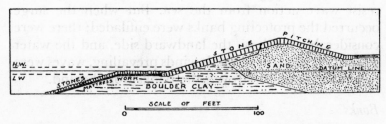

FIG. VII.2—Simplified section of seaward half of main dyke in reclamation of Zuider Zee.

Once the flow of water has been stopped by these means, the permanent embankment can be built. The design of banks varies very widely; Fig. VII.2 is a good example of a modern structure. The essential requirements of a bank are three. First the weight of material must be sufficient to withstand the pressure of the water. Secondly the material should be impervious; but it is required in such large quantities that local supplies will almost invariably be used, and if this is not impervious, a clay core will be required in order to ensure that seepage does not occur; if seepage does start, it is difficult to control, and scour on a large scale is almost certain to follow. The third requirement is a protective apron of stone, either loose 'pitching' or masonry, to withstand the destructive power of the waves.

Engineers who design reclamation schemes have to decide whether they shall consist of large or small enclosures. If the area to be reclaimed can be enclosed by one dyke, which has to be built in any case, the scheme will obviously be cheaper than reclaiming the area piecemeal by a succession of smaller enclosures. Many reclamation schemes, however, have proceeded by stages, often for the reason that a given generation has had the resources, whether financial or of labour, to do only a limited amount; later generations have made their contributions whenever they have been able to do so. There is a practical difficulty in enclosing large areas; the larger the area enclosed the more difficult it must be finally to close the gap when the dyke is near completion. The rush of water is difficult to control, and the accounts of closing some of the Dutch dykes make exciting reading. Modern engineering methods will doubtless make it possible to construct dykes in circumstances in which hitherto it has not been thought possible to build them. But the fact remains that, the larger the reclamation scheme the deeper the water is likely to be. A dyke to enclose the whole of the Wash would need to be built in 100 or more feet of water, but more than 30 per cent of the area is less than 10 feet below chart datum. This is a considerable area, and were the reclamation of the Wash to be contemplated there is little doubt that these shallower parts would be enclosed first leaving the deeper areas for posterity—with their improved knowledge and techniques—to deal with.

Gronyes

Much of our coastline has been preserved because of the timely erection of groynes. They consist in principle of vertical structures erected at an angle with a coastline, as is shown in Fig. VII.3. As the material is moved along the coastline by current action or by oblique waves, and as it is sent up and down the beach by waves, material will be halted against the groynes. Readers will doubtless have seen deposits of shingle lying alongside groynes at many seaside resorts. They will serve no useful purpose if there is not enough material moving along the coastline, or if the current and wave processes do not combine to push it towards the back of the groynes rather than pull it out.

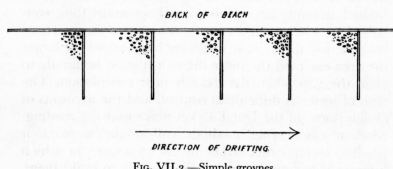

BACK OF BEACH

DIRECTION OF DRIFTING

Fig. VII.3.—Simple groynes.

The principle of protection by groynes being established, it remains only to discuss the form of their construction, that is to say, their lengths, heights and directions. As to the materials to be used, this is usually timber, though masonry, concrete and steel have been used. But ideally groynes should not be regarded as permanent structures; they have done their work when they are filled, or covered by the material that they have trapped, and the time has then come to build others which will collect over a greater distance to seaward, or perhaps to a greater height.

There seems to be no accepted rules among engineers for building groynes: opinions vary very widely, as indeed they must do, for no two engineers have been confronted by exactly the same problem. Some schemes have been successful, others not so, and it has not always been apparent why success or failure has occurred. There have been many instances, however, when systems of groynes have pointed to lessons which future engineers would do well to remember.

Many accept the rule that the distance between successive groyne wings should be roughly equal to their lengths. But what are these lengths to be? There is a large measure of agreement that they should extend to the level of low spring tides. But one authority remarks 'Below L.W.M. [presumably 'low water mark'] the travel of sand goes on almost unimpeded. This travel is one of the most troublesome problems.' Any proposal to limit groynes to the beach above the level of low spring tides is utterly defenceless in terms of efficiency, although the advantages in economy of construction are obvious; it is much more difficult and therefore costly to erect groynes below water than above it. But all the evidence is that the total rate of sand movement in the coastwise direction is greater below the level of low springs than above it. Not only is it covered by water at all times instead of part of the time, but, unless the tidal range is very large, the waves have a greater capacity for getting the sand in suspension, and the longshore currents are greater here than further inshore. The conclusion therefore is that many groynes are now stopped where they might well begin. It is probably the small accumulations of shingle at the top of groyned beaches which create a false impression of the efficacy of groynes; the small amount of shingle lying there proves little except its own existence; indeed it is not unknown for such deposits to suggest a drift in one direction when there is a preponderance of movement of material on the beach as a whole in the opposite direction.

In general there is little advantage in building very

high groynes. Large structures are more vulnerable to wave action and therefore need to be of a very solid construction; there is obviously no point in building them much higher than the highest level normally reached by the sea, and as has just been said it is not the top of the beach which needs the most protection by groynes. Low groynes can be simply constructed, and there appear to be strong reasons for driving short piles with adequate wooden planking. When they have collected material up to the limit of capacity another series could then be constructed. It would not be flattering to the wisdom of those responsible to draw attention to large expensive groynes which have not collected material, but which have gradually been undercut by wave action only to collapse on the beach after serving lives of complete use-lessness. Such groynes can be seen round our coasts, and as monuments of misjudgment they are embarrassingly prominent.

Engineering literature also speculates upon the ideal directions in which groynes should lie with reference to the coastline, and the literature advises us in various places that they should point at right angles to the coast-line or to windward or to leeward. Clearly one of these directions must be right, but it is not clear why groyne directions should be decided in terms of wind behaviour. Certainly the wind is an important factor, but the criterion should be the resultant direction of coastal drifting *due to all causes*. That is to say, the groynes should be so orientated relative to the dominating directions of travel of the bed material that the maximum possible amount of it is trapped. This direction is rarely known and it can be determined only after systematic and thorough observations over a long period—certainly longer than a year.

If oblique groynes are more effective in trapping material than those built at right angles to the coast, they

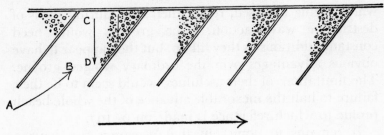

FIG. VII.4.—Oblique groynes.

will also have a greater capacity for holding the material, once it is trapped. Material is pulled back to seaward during the recession of destructive waves, and this recession is down the maximum slope of the beach or at right angles to the coast. Such waves therefore could withdraw material freely from the bays between right-angled groynes, but their action would be impeded by oblique groynes. In Fig. VII.4 it is clear that material can be pushed into the groynes in the direction AB, but the recession of the waves being down the maximum slope of the beach CD the material is likely to stay in the groynes. It is to be noted, however, that the entry will not always be in the direction AB, and in such circumstances the trapping efficiency of the groynes is greatly reduced.

It frequently occurs that during storms material is pulled from between wing groynes and there is one system of groyning which seems to provide an answer to this action (see Fig. VII.5). This consists of triangular boxes which fill up as the material is thrown up; but

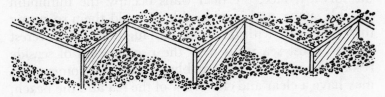

FIG. VII.5.—Box groynes.

193

which, being enclosed, retain their load during spells of destructive wave action. Such groynes would need constant additions as they fill up, but they appear to have obvious advantages over the ordinary winged groyne. The limitations of their usefulness would seem to be their failure to halt the inexorable advance of the whole beach profile to which reference is made on p. 197.

It remains to point out that groyning can have a beneficial effect only on short lengths of coastline. The fact that shingle has been retained at one point means that a place to leeward of it has been deprived of what would normally have come to it. To groyne a whole coastline would presumably have no effect at all on the total conservation of beach material.

Sea Walls

Sea walls are usually a final attempt to deny the sea's advance upon the land; they are extremely expensive to construct and therefore are usually found only in front of valuable property or important sites such as towns or railways. They are often associated with groynes. Many examples will suggest themselves to readers, notably in seaside towns where the sand beach which is the centre of attraction is sharply separated from the residential town at the back of it by the sea wall and possibly the promenade.

The design of sea walls is much influenced by their positions, and by the availability of materials. Walls built recently show interesting variations in the inclination of the forward face. Vertical walls occupy the minimum possible space, and it is possible to build them so strong that they will withstand the onslaught of the severest storms. Most sea walls near the promenades of seaside resorts are vertical, presumably so that the promenaders may have a clear and close view of the sea and the beach, and may have easy access to it by steps. An occasional

modification of the vertical wall is a 'nose' or projecting
ridge along the top of the wall which causes rising waves
and spray to be thrown to seaward (see Fig. VII.6 A).
The usefulness of this device must be limited because the
largest waves are likely to be associated with strong onshore winds, and if the 'nose' threw the sea and spray
upwards and to seaward the wind in all probability
would throw a large proportion of it ashore before it fell
back to sea level.

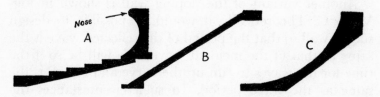

Fig. VII.6.—Some sections of sea walls.

The only advantage of vertical walls is that they
require the minimum of ground space; there are often
good reasons for building walls of greater width, for not
only can they be heavier and placed on more generous
foundations, but the added width makes it possible to
introduce wave-resistant properties which prolong the
life of the wall and at the same time make them more
effective. A vertical wall might have to withstand the full
shock of a breaking wave; it will be seen that it is possible
to build a wider wall so that the energy of the waves is
dissipated gradually, or indeed in such a way that the
wave system tends to destroy itself.

A simple sloping wall (see B in Fig. VII.6) will not be
subject to the battering action of waves; as they travel
up the wall their break will be accelerated, if they have
not already broken, and much of their energy will be
expended in their run up the slope of the wall, the impact
being a glancing rather than a direct blow. There are
many variations of this sloping structure; often the lower

part of the wall is protected by an apron of concrete or masonry on which the waves break, and which prevents scouring at the foot of the wall. An interesting and effective modification is stepping. Fig. VII.6 A shows such a wall; each step absorbs part of the energy of the wave so that the horizontal blow is spread over a considerable part of the structure, and the wave energy is reduced without the large stresses which the single vertical plane of a simple wall must suffer.

Another variant of the sloping wall is shown in Fig. VII.6 C. Theoretically it would be possible to design such a wall so that the period of the reflected wave is the same as that of the incident wave; this will be so if the time for the waves to run up the curve and return is the same as the wave period. In such circumstances the waves near the wall would become standing waves;[1] there would be an 'up and down' and 'in and out' effect as the reflected waves were superimposed on those following them, but the destructive power of the breaking wave would be annulled. The idea is ingenious and can be demonstrated in controlled conditions in a laboratory. Unfortunately the effect cannot be so complete in nature, for the curvature of the wall which might exactly produce a standing wave for a given sea level and a given wave period must obviously produce reflected waves which are out of phase when the sea level changes or the wave period varies. And such changes of course are the rule rather than the exception. If the design is to serve a really useful purpose it would seem advisable to construct it so that its efficiency is greatest when the threat of erosion is greatest; that is for the maximum tide level for the place and the greatest wave period likely to occur.

Vertical walls are sometimes very effectively protected by putting large loose concrete blocks on their seaward

[1] This is known as the Clapotis effect.

faces. These blocks absorb much of the wave energy, so that the impact of each wave is considerably reduced. The process is expensive. The blocks must be so heavy that the waves cannot move them. If they do move two things will happen; first the wall will be damaged by the blows delivered by the blocks; secondly, they themselves will by constant attrition chip one another and so become reduced in size; in time they will be removed entirely by wave and current action just as the material of a shingle beach is bound to be reduced in size.

The usefulness of sea walls is beyond dispute. Large lengths of our coastline have been saved from the sea by protective walls. Yet they must not be regarded as permanent structures. One engineer has said, 'The construction of a sea wall on a sand or shingle foreshore is in itself calculated to bring about the denudation of the beach, and the whole wall may become before long the agent of its own destruction.' This is probably an overstatement. Certainly it is difficult to build walls in exposed places in such a way that the ends are not attacked and enfiladed. But there are other reasons for supposing that a wall cannot permanently stabilize a receding coastline. The erosion does not take place only at the back of the beach. As has been explained earlier when a coastline recedes the beach profile remains remarkably constant, and this profile down to a depth of two or three fathoms perhaps, advances steadily landwards. In Fig. VII.1 a profile represented by AA′ will soon be followed by a general lowering of the beach to BB′ or in due course to CC′. The effect on the wall is inevitable. The presence of the wall does nothing to halt this advance; it merely prevents the profile B′B from extending to B″; this protection is only temporary, and the life of the wall ends when the sea bed reaches the state CC′ if not a little sooner.

The regrettable conclusion is that in the long run man

can do little to prevent erosion; the forces are too great. Temporary palliatives are possible, but their benefits *are* temporary. Any responsible body would probably live to see the benefits of building a sea wall without living to see its destruction. On the other hand, sea walls in many places would not last more than a generation unless their foundations went to such a depth that the cost of the wall was not justified. The economics of coast defences are always a difficult problem; fortunately they do not fall within the scope of this book.

An entirely new method of coastal defence has been tried at Dover. It has for some time been known that the injection of air bubbles into a wave system reduces its height and therefore its energy, but as far as is known the Dover experiment is the first attempt to apply the principle on a large scale. Air distributor vents are sunk on the bottom, and air is pumped to them from compressors on the breakwater. The effect is that during storms a steady stream of bubbles rises like a curtain across the harbour entrance. It is claimed that 'the curtain of bubbles which rapidly ascends to the surface is able to reduce the height of a wave by half, and its "hitting power", or destructive capacity, by a quarter, thus reducing a heavy and dangerous sea to a light sea'.

If one 'curtain' has this effect, successive curtains could presumably produce further diminution of the wave energy. It seems probable that there are practical difficulties in mooring the distributors and in securing the feed pipes. These problems, though difficult, are not insoluble, though the solutions might be very costly. The writer does not know the cost of constructing and maintaining such an installation; certainly it has some intriguing possibilities.

APPENDICES

BIBLIOGRAPHY

INDEX

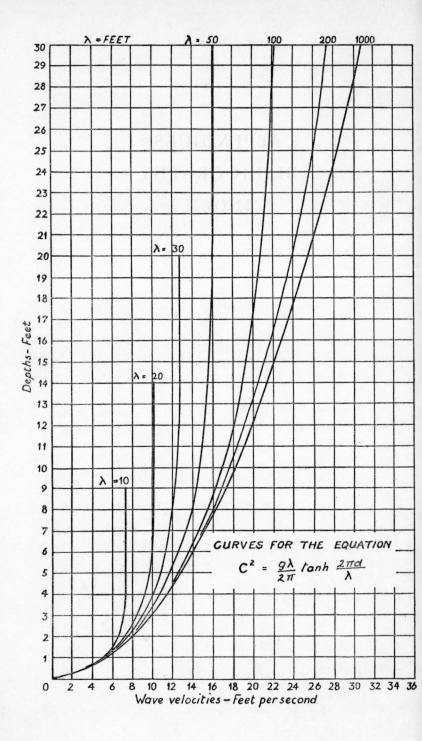

λ = FEET   λ = 50   100   200   1000

λ = 30

λ = 20

λ = 10

Depths – Feet

CURVES FOR THE EQUATION

$$C^2 = \frac{g\lambda}{2\pi} \tanh \frac{2\pi d}{\lambda}$$

Wave velocities – Feet per second

APPENDIX A

The diagram opposite may be of interest for two reasons. First because the fundamental mathematical formula in it has an important meaning which may not be understood by some readers in its non-graphical form. Secondly, it shows how the expression may be plotted in a form which is quick and easy to use. For practical purposes the curves would be drawn on a larger scale, and for a wider selection of wave lengths. The gap between 200 and 1,000 feet, for instance, is much too great. In wide seas there are very often waves whose lengths lie between these limits with which it might be necessary to deal.

The curves show two aspects of wave behaviour which are of some importance. It will be observed that when the wave-length/water-depth ratio is small, wave velocity is a function of wave length alone. The curves for wave lengths 10, 20, 30 and 50 feet show that at their upper limits the velocities are uniform; it is only when the wave-length/water-depth ratio becomes large that the velocity is affected by the shoaling of the water. It should be noticed in passing that before the waves come to rest they break, a circumstance not indicated in the diagram; this does not appear to cause any marked change in the wave velocity.

The second point to observe is that when the wave-length/water-depth is large, variations in wave length become of secondary importance; it is rather the water depth which is the deciding factor. In the diagram, for instance, for the limited depth range shown, the relation

APPENDICES

between water depth and wave velocity for wave lengths
of 200 feet and 1,000 feet varies very little.

The curves are simple to use if the necessary quantities
can be determined. Wave lengths are never easy to
measure in nature; sometimes they can be measured in
air photographs, but only when the incidence of the light
on the sea surface is favourable, and when only one
single wave train can be identified.

The formula assumes that the depth is the 'still water'
depth, and that any depth is the mean for a whole wave
length.

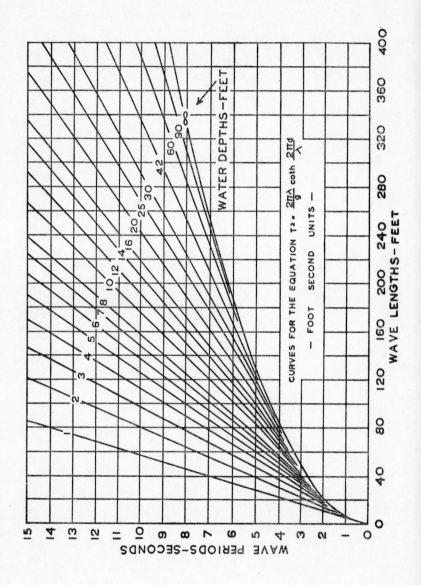

WAVE LENGTHS - FEET

WAVE PERIODS - SECONDS

WATER DEPTHS - FEET

CURVES FOR THE EQUATION $T^2 = \frac{2\pi\lambda}{g} \coth \frac{2\pi d}{\lambda}$

— FOOT SECOND UNITS —

APPENDIX B

From $\dfrac{\lambda}{2} = cT$

and $\qquad\qquad C^2 = \dfrac{g\lambda}{2\pi} \tanh \dfrac{2\pi d}{\lambda}$

putting $\qquad\qquad c = \dfrac{\lambda}{T}$

we have $\qquad \left(\dfrac{\lambda}{T}\right)^2 = \dfrac{g\lambda}{2\pi} \tanh \dfrac{2\pi d}{\lambda}$

or $\qquad\qquad T^2 = \dfrac{2\pi\lambda}{g} \coth \dfrac{2\pi d}{\lambda}$

The curves give a relation between wave period, wave length and a selected number of water depths.

When one single wave train is running, it is a simple matter to determine the wave period with the aid of a stop-watch, or even an ordinary watch with a second hand. Once this is known the wave lengths in various depths are easily ascertained.

The curves were used extensively during the war of 1939–45 for the determination of water depths and beach gradients as follows: suppose that we have found the scale of an air photograph and that the length of waves in deep water is 250 feet. For a curve $d = \infty$, a wave length of 250 corresponds with the period $t = 7$ seconds. This of course is the period of the wave system whatever the depth may be. If now we measure the lengths of the waves as they shorten in their progress towards the water line we can easily deduce the depths. For instance, for $t = 7$ seconds, and

$$\lambda = 190 \qquad d = 30$$
$$\lambda = 130 \qquad d = 12$$
$$\lambda = 100 \qquad d = 7$$

It would be misleading to give the impression that this is a precise way of determining water depths; it is not. There are several practical difficulties. For instance, as has been pointed out already it is rarely the case that only one wave train exists at any given time and place. Again, waves are not always well defined, so that it is not always possible to measure them accurately; and the curves themselves show that the rate of change of wave length to depth is unfavourable as the depths increase.

But useful work was done in this way during the war, and it has been used successfully in peace in surf conditions when small boats with echo-sounders operate only with great difficulty.

APPENDIX C

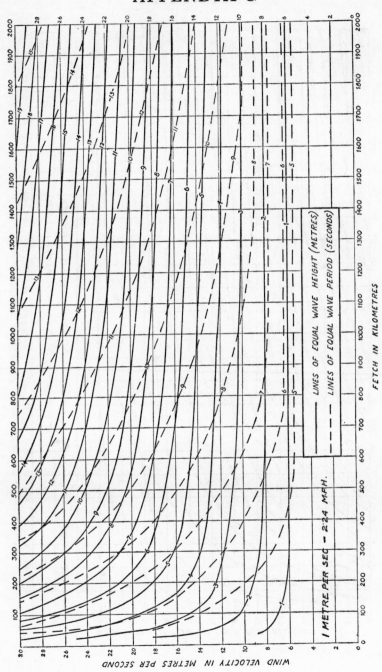

LINES OF EQUAL WAVE HEIGHT (METRES)

LINES OF EQUAL WAVE PERIOD (SECONDS)

1 METRE PER SEC = 2·24 M.P.H.

FETCH IN KILOMETRES

WIND VELOCITY IN METRES PER SECOND

APPENDIX D

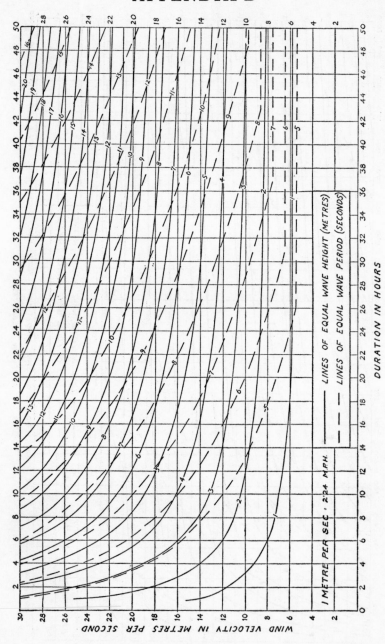

LINES OF EQUAL WAVE HEIGHT (METRES)

LINES OF EQUAL WAVE PERIOD (SECONDS)

1 METRE PER SEC = 2·24 M.P.H.

DURATION IN HOURS

WIND VELOCITY IN METRES PER SECOND

APPENDICES C AND D

THE EFFECT OF FETCH[1] ON WAVE HEIGHT

It is observable that for a wind of given strength the wave height increases with the distance over which the wind has blown. For this,

$$H_f = 0.105 \sqrt{f} \qquad . \qquad . \qquad (5)$$

where H_f represents the heights of the waves in centimetres, and f represents the fetch in centimetres.

This means that the highest waves that one would expect to find generated over a fetch of 100 km. (62 miles) would be 3.2 metres, or 10 feet; over a fetch of 2,000 km. it would be 14.6 metres, or 48 feet.

THE EFFECT OF FETCH ON WAVE VELOCITY

The longer the wind blows, the more energy is transmitted by the wind to the water surface, and the faster do the waves move; at the same time the lengths and periods of the waves increase. The curves in Appendix C show how wave height and period increase with an

---

[1] 'Fetch' is variously understood to mean the distance in the direction in which the wind is blowing to the next land, that is, the maximum possible distance over which a wind from that direction might be able to generate waves, or, the distance over which generating winds from a given direction have in fact blown; this will often, of course, be less than the distance defined first. I have used 'fetch' in both senses, and I think that the context makes clear which is meant.

increase of fetch. The lengths of the waves of any given period can be calculated from:

$$T^2 = \frac{2\pi\lambda}{g} \coth \frac{2\pi d}{\lambda} \qquad . \qquad . \qquad (6)$$

in which $\qquad T =$ the wave period

$\qquad\qquad\qquad d =$ the water depth

and $\qquad\qquad \lambda =$ the wave length.

Curves to facilitate the use of this equation will be found in Appendix B. If velocities are required they can be obtained from $\lambda = cT$ (1).

WIND VELOCITY AND WAVE HEIGHT

For a given fetch, the harder it blows, the higher will the waves be. This is generally true, and Appendix C[1] gives a useful correlation for this rate of growth. In very high winds it sometimes happens that wave tops become white horses, the crests of the waves being blown off. Such winds rarely occur, however, and in any case the phenomenon is not important in beach problems. Rossby and Montgomery suggest:

$$H_m = \frac{0.3\, u^2}{g} \qquad . \qquad . \qquad . \qquad (7)$$

As a relationship between H_m, the greatest wave that can occur for a given fetch in centimetres where u is the velocity of a uniform wind in centimetres per second.

WIND VELOCITY AND WAVE VELOCITY

A high wind, other things being equal, will generate longer and therefore more rapid waves than a gentle

---

[1] I am indebted to the Hydrographic Department of the United States Navy for permission to reproduce equation (5) and the curves in Appendices C and D. These first appeared in a war time publication *Wind Waves and Swell* by Sverdup and Munk.

wind. The curves in Appendix C show the rate of growth in varying circumstances. Jeffreys is of the opinion that waves can grow only if their velocity is less than that of the generating wind; which means, in effect, that the limiting factor of wave velocities (assuming sufficient fetch) is the velocity of the generating wind. This is a conclusion with which some other authorities disagree.

THE EFFECT OF WIND DURATION ON WAVE HEIGHT AND WAVE VELOCITY

Within a large ocean the wind will not blow uniformly in speed or direction over the whole area, nor will it blow for an indefinite time. The heights and lengths of the waves will be influenced by the length of time during which the particular wind conditions have obtained. The curves in Appendix D show the effect of wind duration in widely differing circumstances.

Appendices C and D should be carefully examined. The information shown there is considerable as well as interesting and important. If used for specific problems, however, they should be used with caution, not because they are not reliable, but because in using them the 'known' quantities are rarely accurately known, so that the results read from the curves will be correspondingly open to doubt. For instance, it is rarely possible to say with certainty of a particular storm what its duration has been, or what the wind velocity has been; and it is certain that during the storm the wind velocity was not constant.

The diagrams are based on a large amount of observations, and indicate the rate of growth of wave periods and heights in differing conditions of wind. Each diagram shows the effect of winds whose velocities are between 0 and 30 metres per second (67 m.p.h.), but whereas Appendix C plots the effect of fetch, Appendix D shows the effect of the duration of the winds. As is to be expected the forms of the curves are very similar. Some interesting factors are shown. For instance (see Appendix C), a wind of 18 metres per second will generate waves 2 metres high in a distance of 25 miles, but a wind of 8 metres per second would need to blow over a distance of 650 miles in order to produce waves of the same height but it is incapable of producing higher waves.

A comparable state of affairs can be seen in Appendix D. Here it is shown that a wind of velocity 24 metres per second will produce waves 2 metres high in an hour; but winds of 9 metres per second would need to blow for 19 hours to produce the same height, and it is doubtful whether winds of velocity 8 metres per second can ever produce such waves.

The general inference of the curves is clear; the stronger the wind and the longer it blows, or the larger the fetch, the larger and higher the waves will be, subject to the kind of limitation that has already been referred to.

CONVERSION TABLES

Metres per sec.	1	2	3	4	5	6	7	8	9
M.P.H.	2·2	4·5	6·7	9·0	11·2	13·4	15·7	17·9	20·1

Kilometres	1	2	3	4	5	6	7	8	9
Miles	·62	1·24	1·86	2·48	3·11	3·73	4·35	4·97	5·59

BIBLIOGRAPHY

Admiralty. *Admiralty Navigation Manual.*
AGATINO D'ARRIGO. *Ricerche sul Regime dei Litorali nel Mediterraneo.*
Association d'Oceanographie Physique. Union Géodésique et Géophysique International. *Secular Variation of Sea Level.* Publication Scientifique No. 13, 1954.
BAGNOLD, R. A. *The Physics of Blown Sand and Desert Dunes.*
BARKER, N., and DOYLE, D. 'A method of recording the direction of travel of ocean swell.' *Deep-Sea Research,* 1956, Vol. 3.
BARKER, N., and URSELL, F. 'The generation and propagation of ocean waves and swell.' Phil. Trans. of the Royal Society A., 24 February 1948.
Beach Erosion Board, U.S.A. *A Study of Progressive Oscillatory Waves in Water.* Technical Report No. 1 and others.
—— *An Experimental Study of Submarine Sandbars.* Technical Report No. 3.
BOURCART JACQUES. *Les frontières de l'océan.*
BOURCART and AUZEL. 'L'oceanographie au secours des plages françaises.' *La Revue Française,* No. 32.
CAREY, A. E., and OLIVER, F. W. *Tidal Lands.*
CARRUTHERS, J. N. 'A device for observing bottom currents.' *Fishing News,* No. 2362, 25 July 1958.
CORKAN, R. H. *Storm Surges.* The Dock and Harbour Authority, February 1948.
CORNISH VAUGHAN (1). *Ocean Waves.*
—— (2) 'On the grading of the Chesil Beach shingle.' Proc. Dorset Natural History and Antiquarian Field Club, 1898.
DAVIDSSON, J. *Investigations of Sand Movements using Radio-active Sand.* LUND, Studies in Geography, Ser. A, Physical Geography, No. 12.
DOODSON, A. T. (1) *Meteorological Perturbations of Sea Levels and Tides.* Monthly Notices of R.A.S., Geophysical Supplement, April 1924.
—— (2) 'Tides and storm surges in a long uniform gulf.' Proceedings of the Royal Society A., Vol. 237, 1956.
DURST, C. S. 'The relationship between current and wind.' *Quarterly Journal of the Royal Meteorological Society,* Vol. 2, No. 210.
GORDON, D. L. 'Mean Sea Level around the British Isles.' *Journal of the Royal Institute of Chartered Surveyors,* July 1957.
GUILCHER, A. *Morphologie Littorale et Sous Marine.*
HIDAKA, K. 'Study of ocean waves by stereophotogrammetry.' *Journal of Oceanography Imperial Marine Obs. Kobe,* Vol. 11, No. 4, 1939.

BIBLIOGRAPHY

HJULSTRÖM, FILIP (1) *Transportation of Detritus by Moving Water.*
—— (2) *Studies of the Morphological Activity of Rivers as illustrated by the River Fyris.*
HOLMES, A. *Principles of Physical Geology.*
HUNT, A. R. (1) 'On the action of waves on sea beaches and sea bottoms.' Proceedings of the Royal Dublin Society, 1884.
—— (2) *Denudation and Deposition by the Agency of Sea Waves.*
Hydrographic Dept., Admiralty (1) *The Admiralty Tide Tables.*
—— (2) *Admiralty Manual of Hydrographic Surveying.*
INMAN, D. L., and IRWIN, W. H. *Currents in the Surf Lane.* Scripps Inst. of Oceanography Series, No. 560.
INMAN, D. L., and CHAMBERLAIN, T. K. 'Tracing Beach Sand Movement with Irradiated Quartz.' *Journal of Geographical Research*, Vol. 64, 1.
JOLY, J. *The Surface-History of the Earth.*
JOHNSON, D. W. *Shore Processes and Shoreline Development.*
KIDSON, C. (with CARR and SMITH). 'Further experiments using radio-active methods to detect the movement of shingle over the seabed and alongshore.' *G.H.*, CXXIV, Part 2.
KING, C. A. M. (1) 'Depth of disturbance of sand in sea beaches by waves.' *Journal of Sedimentary Petrology*, Vol. 21.
—— (2) *The Movement of Sand on Beaches by Wave and other action.*
KING, C. A. M., and WILLIAMS, W. W. 'The formation and movement of sandbars by wave action.' *G.J.*, Vol. CXII.
LAKE and RASTALL. *A Textbook of Geology.*
LAMB, Sir Horace. *Hydrodynamics.*
LEWIS, W. V. 'The Evolution of Shoreline Curves.' Proceedings of the Geologists' Association, Vol. XLIX, 1938.
LEWIS, W. V., and BALCHIN, W. G. V. 'Past Sea Levels at Dungeness.' *G.J.*, Vol. XCVI, No. 4.
LONGUET-HIGGINS, M. S. (1) *The Refraction of Sea Waves in Shallow Water.* National Institute of Oceanography.
—— (2) 'On the Statistical Distribution of the Heights of Sea Waves.' *Sears Foundation, Journal of Marine Research*, Vol. XI, No. 3.
MINIKIN. *Coast Erosion and Protection.*
MARMER. *The Tides.*
NANSEN, FRIDTJOF. 'Oscillations of Shorelines.' *G.J.*, December 1905.
PAZDRO, Dr. ZDISLAW. *Pólwysep Hel i jego genza.*
ROBINSON and CLOET. 'Coastal Evolution in Sandwich Bay.' Proc. of Geologists' Association, Vol. 64.
RUSSELL and MACMILLAN. *Waves and Tides.*
SCHUMACHER, A. *Deutsche Atlantische Exped. Meteor 1925–7.* Berlin, 1939.
SHEPPARD, F. P. *Submarine Geology.*
SHEPPARD, F. P., 'Nearshore Water Circulation Related to Bottom Topography and Wave Refraction.' Trans. American Geophysical Union, Vol. 31.
SHEPPARD, T. *The Lost Towns of the Yorkshire Coast.*
STEERS, J. A. (1) *The Coastline of England and Wales.*

BIBLIOGRAPHY

STEERS, J. A. (2) 'The Coast of East Anglia.' *New Naturalist*, No. 6, 1949.
—— (3) 'The East Coast Floods.' *G.J.*, CXIX.
—— (4) 'The Culbin Sands and Burqhead Bay.' *G.J.*, XC.
—— (5) 'The Rate of Sedimentation on Salt Marshes on Scolt Head Island, Norfolk.' *Geological Magazine*, LXXV, January 1938.
STEERS, J. A. (and others). *Scolt Head Island*.
STEERS, J. A., and SMITH, D. B. 'Detection of Movement on the Sea Floor by Radio Active Methods.' *G.J.*, CXXII, 3.
SVERDRUP, JOHNSON and FLEMING. *The Oceans*.
SVERDRUP and MUNK. *Wind, Waves and Swell. A Basic Theory for Forecasting*.
VALENTIN, H. 'Present Vertical Movements of the British Isles.' *G.J.*, CXIX.
WALTERS, J. K. A. *Distribution of Heights in Waves*. N.Z. Oceanographic Committee Publication No. 11.
WHEELER, W. H. *The Sea Coast*.
WILLIAMS, W. W. (1) 'The determination of gradients of enemy held Beaches.' *G.J.*, CIX.
—— (2) 'An East Coast Survey.' *G.J.*, CXXII.

INDEX

Aberdeen, eustatic changes at, 37
Aberdovey, 120
Admiralty Tide Tables, 161
Ailsa Craig, 10
Air photographs, 116, 158
Albania, coast of, 119
Alexander, N., 179
Amphibious operations, 1
Andrew, E. W., 109
Arches, 146
Arkell, W. A., 24, 124

Bagnold, R. A., 26, 96, 100
Banks, as sea defences, 187
Barchans, 99
Barmouth, 120
Barrier islands, 38, 128
Bars, 5, 110, 120; offshore, 62, 109, 159; swash, 109, 121; crescentic, 112
Beaches, 105; gradients, determination of, 161, 206; bowshaped form of, 118; nourishment of, 5; profiles, summer and winter, 64, 106; raised, 33, 37; sand, 29, 64; shingle, 64, 65, 122
Benacre Ness, 133
Biscay, dune movement in, 101
Bishop Rock lighthouse, 51
Blackpool, 116, 165
Blyth, Northumberland, 2
Bob Hall's sands, 151
Botanists, 152
Bothnia, eustatic changes in, 32
Bourcart, J., 7, 39
Branksome Chine, 47
Brest, tidal curve, 74

Bristol Channel, 72
Bubble breakwater, 198

Carruthers, J. N., 179
Celsius, 32
Ceylon, river mouths, 2
Charts, hydrographic, 157
Chesil bank, 5, 15, 24, 118, 123, 131
Christchurch bay, 78, 147
Civitavecchia, 30
Clapotis effect, 196
Cliffs, erosion of, 9, 146
Coal waste on beaches, 7, 18
Colloidal deposits, 18
Constructive waves, 63
Coral, 120, 121
Coriolis force, 91
Corkan, R. H., 82
Cornish, V., 7
Corrievreckan, 77
Covehithe, 84, 107, 155; -ness, 84; cliffs, erosion of, 13, 84
Crescentic bars, 112
Culbin sands, 101
Current meters, 177
Currents, 79, 135; measurement of, 79, 173
Currents, ocean, 78, 91
Curves, shoreline, 118

Datum level, for soundings, 157
Davidson, J., 181
Davis, W. M., 7
Deacon, G. E. R., 53, 173
Deauville Plage, 107
Defences, sea, 185

INDEX

Deltas, 144
Densities, of beach materials, 18
Dept. of Hydraulics Research, 8
Destructive waves, 63
Dhu Heartach lighthouse, 51
Disturbance depth, of sand on beaches, 27
Dominant waves, 69
Doodson, A. T., 82
Dover, cliffs of, 10, 146
Dunbar, eustatic changes, 37
Dundee, eustatic changes, 37
Dunes, 6, 99
Dungeness, 5, 14, 118, 133
Dunwich, 13, 86
Dykes, 189

Eccles church, 2
Echo-sounder, 170
Ekman current meter, 2
Emergence, shores of, 31, 37
Enclosures, sizes of, 189
End effect, the, 187, 197
Engineers, xiv, 189
Erosion, prevalence of, 147; rate of, 87
Etangs, 38, 129
Eustatic changes, 31, 32

Fascines, 187
Fenlands, 187
Fetch, of waves, 45, 209
Flamborough Head, 10
Flexure of coasts, 39
Floods, 1953, 85, 86, 187
Frische Nehrung, 126
Fryer, D. H., xvii

Gauge, tide, 32
Gilbert, G. K., 121
Gradients, of beaches, 22, 29; determination of, 161, 206
Gravity, effect of, 40
Groynes, 186, 189; box, 193; orientation of, 192

Haffs, 120, 127

Headlands, 27; loose, 133; wave action on, 68
Hidaka, K., 163
Hjulström, F., 19
Holderness, 13
Holland, dunes in, 101; sea defences, 188
Hurst castle and spit, 78
Hwang Ho delta, 145
Hydrographic Dept., Admiralty, 157, 172
Hydrographic surveys, 157, 167

Ice caps, 31
Ilfracombe, 72
Islands, barrier, 38, 128
Isostatic adjustment, 32

Johnson, D. W., 7, 115, 120, 131
Jointing, effects of, 10
Jumping, of sand grains, 97

Kidson, C., 181
King, C. A. M., 27, 96, 111
Krakatoa eruption, 42
Kurische Nehrung, 126

Lake, P., 25
Land's End, 10
Le Havre, tidal curve, 74
Lewis, W. V., 118
Linnaeus, 32
Liverpool Observatory and Tidal Inst., 82
Logships, drifting, 175
Lowestoft, sandbanks off, 2

Manual of Tides, Admiralty, 161
Maps, use of, 154
Marks, reference, for surveys, 164
Marram grass, 100
Marshes, 149
Mass transport—of waves, 57
Meteorological effects, 34, 76, 79, 92
Meters, current, 177
Mierzega Hel, 126
Mississippi delta, 145

INDEX

Monte Argentario, 130
Morib, Malaya, 16
Mud, 16, 17, 29, 149
Mundesley, 13

National Institute of Oceanography, 8, 53
Needles, the, 10, 146
Nehrungen, 109, 120, 125
Newlyn, tide gauge, 37
Nile delta, 145
North Sea, the, 17; surges in, 79, 95

Offshore bar, 62, 109; double, 111
Offshore winds, 94
Orfordness, 79, 120, 129, 133
Orogenic movements, 31
Ostend, windblown sand at, 96
Ott current meter, 177

Pakefield, cliffs at, 140
Parabolic profile of beaches, 105
Pentland Firth, 77, 94
Peterhead, storm damage at, 50
Photographs, air, 158
Piling, sheet, 186
Platform, wave cut, 12
Plunge point and line of waves, 59
Porthkerry beach, 22
Pressure, atmospheric, implications of, 34
Pressures in waves, 12
Prevalent waves, 69
Profiles, beach, 65

Radio-active methods, 180
Raised beaches, 33, 37
Rastall, 25
Raz de marée, 76, 99
Reclamation of land, 189
Refraction of waves, 66
Rest, angle of (cliffs), 13
Revision, of charts and maps, 157
Ridges, shingle, 15, 22
Ripples, 29, 97, 140
Roberts radio current meter, 178
Runnels and bars, 115, 159

Salerno Bay, 1
Saltations of sand, 97
Sand, 5, 25; grain sizes, 15, 20; layers, thickness of, 28; sources of, 26; transport by wind, 96
Sandstone, old red, 10
Scania, 33
Schumacher, A., 163
Scolt Island, 101, 140
Scouring, 187
Seaton Sluice, 25, 95, 102
Seifs, 99
Selsey Bill, 133, 134
Settling velocities, 18
Shingle, 5, 21
Shingle beaches, 21, 122; gradients, 22; wastage of, 24
Shingle ridges, 15, 22; wave action on, 23, 65
Shingles, the, 78
Sorting of beach materials, 14; horizontal, 15; vertical, 16
Spits, 120, 125; recurved, 140
Sound, velocity of in water, 170
Southampton, tides, 75
Southwold, 13
Start Point, 10
Steers, J. A., 7, 118, 134, 140
Submergence, shores of, 31, 38
Subtense methods of survey, 168
Summer beach profiles, 106
Surf, 59
Surf bathers, 60
Surges, 79, 95
Surveys, methods of, 164
Suspension, material in, 21, 70
Sussex, chalk cliffs, 12
Swash bar, 109, 121
Swell, 46

Tiber, mouth of, 145
Tidal streams, 71, 76
Tide gauge, 33
Tides, 62, 71
Tombolos, 131, 149
Transport, mass, 57
Traps, sand, 98

Tsunamis, 76

Undertow, 61

Valentin, H., 33
Vierlingh, A., 188

Walls, sea, 186, 194
Warping, 187
Wash, the, 189
Water level, determination of, 167
Watt current meter, 177
Waves, 40, 89
Waves, breaking, 59; constructive, 63; destructive, 63; dominant, 69; energy of, 42, 48; form of, 44, 53, 54; heights, 46, 47; mass transport in, 57; measurement of, 90, 172; oblique, 67; particle motion in, 55; periods of, 47; prevalent, 69; refraction of, 51, 66; short crested, 52; stability of, 44; steepness, 44; trains of, 43; unbroken, 56, 59; velocities of, 45, 54; volcanic, 42

Wheeler, W. H., 17, 19
Wick, storm damage at, 50
Wind, effect of, 78, 88; observations, 47
Winter beach profiles, 106

Yare, mouth of, 79, 137